Best Wishes

Marcia Moore

Mark Douglas

Al

A

DIET, SEX and YOGA

Diet, Sex and Yoga

MARCIA MOORE · MARK DOUGLAS

PHOTOGRAPHS OF MARCIA MOORE
BY MARK DOUGLAS

ARCANE PUBLICATIONS
YORK CLIFFS, MAINE 03902

FIRST EDITION
Library of Congress Catalog Card Number: 66–28086
Manufactured in the United States of America

Distributed by the Fifth Kingdom Foundation

To our parents
with
love, affection and gratitude

Contents

Introduction

THIS STARTED OUT AS A DIET BOOK, written in response to innumerable requests for guidance in losing weight. The urgency of these pleas made us realize that fat can not be taken lightly. For millions it has become a matter of life and death.

Almost immediately our research disclosed that what is needed by the overweight person is not recipes for eating but recipes for not eating. The fundamental need is not to make dieting easier but to make the dieter stronger in body, mind and will, so that he naturally craves what is best for him.

The word diet derives from a Greek word meaning "manner of living." Sex, the process which brings us to birth, reveals the workings of the life-force in us. Yoga is an all-inclusive "way of life," a search for self-realization whose goal is union of the individual spirit with the supreme spirit of the universe. Rightly used these successive and complementary modes of expression serve to release the potential within every human being.

The food we eat gives contentment to body and senses. Sexual pleasure affords not only immediate gratification, but the possibility of lasting joy involving the total personality. Yoga leads to the ultimate bliss of identification with all creation. Food relates to what we incorporate from the lower kingdoms of nature. Sex determines our relations with other human beings. Yoga concerns our relationship to that which is above and beyond ourselves and which incorporates us within the larger scheme of existence. Together they involve our attitudes toward ourselves, toward others, and toward the universe.

How can a person integrate a subject as pragmatic as food with one as broad as sex and as abstract as yoga? They seem to pull us in different directions. Yet each of us is a nexus of these three tendencies, being motivated by instincts for physical survival, reproduction and self-development. For the sake of health and growth we must seek ways of combining the scattered segments of our being into a creative synthesis.

In this book we discuss attitudes about the body and elucidate applicable techniques of control by means of diet, exercise, deep breathing, relaxation and creative visualization. These same methods serve equally well for people to whom food is no problem, but who wish to stay in shape and attain a higher level of health, efficiency and enthusiasm. Our aim has been not just to present techniques for maintaining normalcy, but to point the way toward becoming superior individuals, even if the path runs contrary to convention. Essentially we are talking not just about diet, sex and yoga, but about your life.

PART ONE

Diet, Sizing Your Life

1

Reverse Effort

LET US BEGIN WHERE OUR PROBLEMS BEGIN — with appetite. What essentially do we crave? And what do we crave it for?

All of us have secret yearnings to be handsome or beautiful, slender or shapely, with all the self-assurance and poise that conjures up the image of attractiveness. But for what reason do we want to be this ideal person? Is it in order to gratify alternate appetites for praise, attention and status? Or is it because we aspire to develop into more vital, inspired and worthwhile human beings?

Since food is taken into ourselves it can become a symbolic substitute for the many benefits we desire to incorporate. But if the purpose of eating is forgotten, and satisfying the senses becomes an end in itself, the result is over-indulgence, a weight problem, and the negation of the good sought. Then comes "the diet."

The trouble with most diets is the psychology of the dieter. Since the difficulty has often been caused by using food to compensate for other lacks, there is nothing to fall back on to compensate for the newly imposed lack of food itself. Our efforts are subverted from the very start. If, therefore, we long to enlarge the ego by diminishing size, it is questionable whether any diet will work permanently. Instead, an under-lying sense of deprivation will make the body's demands for food all the more importunate.

Endeavoring to cure a condition symptomatic of insecurity by provoking further deprivation, not only makes most diets notoriously futile, but contributes one more cog to what already constitutes a veritable clockwork of vicious circles. Ceaselessly we slave to be free, labor for our labor-saving devices, feel compelled to produce increasing numbers of things to take care of the things we already have, and thus grow weary in the quest for sufficient strength to endure the tedium of being amused by ever more novel diversions.

Must we purchase luxuries at the cost of necessities? Are our pretty gadgets worth the price they demand in leisure, fresh air, solitude, space to expand and grow? Many of us are faced with the final irony of discovering that the pleasures of eating must be bought at the price of health, contradicting the comfortable conviction that fat babies are healthier and that plenty of good rich food makes us stronger.

The illogic of these dilemmas in which we find ourselves enmeshed is rendered more poignant by the fact that we think we're well-educated, intellectually enlightened and busy doing good. Indeed, we are gnawed with guilt if not accomplishing worthwhile things, yet hardly count the time spent in illness, lethargy, false starts and unnecessary journeys toward goals which afford no real contentment but only necessitate the pursuit of more elusive or illusory gratifications.

Throughout history men have justified wars by saying it is necessary to kill to prevent killing, despoil lands to bring peace and raise taxes for ultimate prosperity. In the same way men wage a civil war with their bodies making them victims of endless frustration and dissipation in their need to be loved.

A preoccupation with external appearance by attending incessantly to intricacies of diet, elimination, complexion care, odorizing and deodorizing, dressing and undressing, will never solve the basic problem of man divided against himself. These artifices often do not show any real love for the body and, in extreme form can demonstrate an actual fear of all that is natural and free.

Almost invariably women spend increasing time bleaching, dying, teasing and stiffening their hair into curvaceous forms as their figures slide into middle-aged dumpiness. Their clothing bills rise as their flesh sags. We can only speculate what the difference might be if gymnasiums and health studios were as popular as hairdressing salons and clothing stores, but surely real beauty would not be the loser. On the other hand their male counterparts are more likely to seek diversion with alcohol, indulgence in heavy food, obsessive work and equally obsessive recreations.

In modern society it seems that only the youthful and slender or those who decorate the pages of glossy magazines, can dare remain free and spontaneous. They are the ones whose attunement to their bodies is sufficiently "on key" to permit them to forget themselves in the joy and immediacy of doing as they please. These golden people appear to be having so much fun, and they look wonderful even when windblown or emerging dripping from the surf of some eternally sunlit beach.

To understand why our most urgent desires so often come to naught, we must consider the universal principle which the philosopher Alan Watts has termed "The Law of Reverse Effort." According to this law we can deny ourselves the things we want most, simply by wanting them too much. The tighter fingers grasp the less they hold; the more we conserve our strength the less of it we have. The longer we hold our breath the shorter it becomes, but as soon as we give it up we have it again.

An example is the holy man who, in renouncing all worldly possessions and retreating into solitude and meditation, finds that the whole world gives of itself to him. Food and flowers are cast at his feet. Disciples endure every hardship to serve him. Lasting traditions grow up about his casual remarks such as no politician could deliberately construct. All the saints and sages of the world have agreed that we must lose ourselves to find our Selves; the seed must die that the plant may grow, and the plant in turn die to release its new seed. This is how life goes on.

The law of reverse effort can be summed up by saying that we can have anything, absolutely anything that we earn, deserve and need, providing we know how to give it away again. The only justification for ownership is creative use. As long as we hold on to nothing, everything can flow through us, and flow increasingly. The best analogy is that of a pump. The more it gives out the more it can take in and pass along.

Success in dieting and weight control is possible only when the balance of our endeavors is shifted, not just from taking in to giving out, but regulated to become a continuous experience of sharing in higher purposes. One must feel connected to people, nature, and to life itself. The probability of shedding or redistributing excess poundage depends on the extent to which a person can overcome his repressive and inhibitive nature and become an open, expressive participator in nature's bounty.

These may seem harsh words to the poor soul who has for years struggled unsuccessfully with a weight problem. Since the condition is plain for all to see, it should be stated plainly that it is utterly impossible for anyone to change on the outside without first making an initiating change within. (Even the layers of fat grow outward from the stomach and alimentary canal.) That we are what we eat is only a minor truism. That we are what we think and feel is a fundamental truth. Energy follows thought. In this there should be encouragement rather than despair because anyone who can control his attitude can be positively transformed.

One of the main reasons for this book was the observation that all the people who had lost large amounts of weight and *kept* the pounds off (not a large number compared with those who had tried without visible success) possessed one outstanding quality in common. This attribute has not to our knowledge been remarked upon in the numerous diet books on the market. What had happened was that the successful dieters were all, in one way or another, engaged in feeding and serving others. No one had suggested it. They had just felt compelled to make a special effort in behalf of someone in need. Some of the dieters began to teach principles of nutrition, baking and giving away wheat-germ bread and squeezing quarts of raw vegetable juice for friends with health problems. One adopted a war orphan, another helped feed the children in a local hospital. It was not easy, for many had to force themselves at the beginning, but they did it. Once the pump was primed, enthusiasm for their new interests flowed forth.

It often happened that these solicitous attentions to other people's physical needs were made by those who could least afford it. The effort was undertaken in a sacrificial spirit. In some mysterious manner this willing self-deprivation was compensated for with the desired loss of weight.

In ancient times men laid their choicest lambs and bullocks on the altar beseeching divine favor. Similarly today, some meaningful sacrifice is required. This is why fasting, if regular and controlled, works so well. Not only are calories reduced and the digestive system rested but an internal purge and cleansing of the whole psyche results. It is necessary to give something up to let in the flood tide of available assistance. If, for the sake of having a beautiful body, a person is unwilling to make a sacrifice, preferably one which helps others, then the chances are he would hardly succeed in dieting anyway. In this way a diet counsellor or well-wishing friend can judge the measure of sincerity and know whether to bolster the dieter's efforts or remain discreetly silent.

The fact that dieting involves a moral issue is another point on which most experts remain quiet. The issue of right or wrong is positively denied in favor of the theory that overeating, like alcoholism, is a kind of sickness against which the poor victim may be helpless. Possibly an inability to see that the moral law of give and take plays some part in the problem, is itself a kind of sickness. Gluttony may no longer be considered one of the seven deadly sins but we can question the implication of advertisements for food that eating is practically a virtue and bolsters the national economy as well. Surely something is sadly amiss when a society of people so frequently soft, pudgy and flabby exists in a world where at least half the people (even those not on diets) go to bed hungry. In the face of world misery today have we the *right* to be overstuffed?

Moralizing is considered bad taste nowadays. Probably this is a good thing considering the abuses, even the downright "immorality" of the ethical standards and rules which have served the world so poorly in the past. Now, with the present freedom explosion, men have found courage to declare that just because an abuse is old, it is not necessarily sacred. With the breakdown of traditional codes of behavior, people are being forced to reject the authorities to search for values in their own minds and hearts, and to decide what is really real for them as self-determining individuals. Thus, the new morality will have to emerge from direct experience and concern itself with what each one discovers for himself.

But the great law of cause and effect, (which may also be stated that every action produces an equal and opposite reaction), still exists as surely as the laws of gravity and electricity. If overweight has become a national problem, there has to be *some* reason for it. Until we begin to deal with this basic cause the phenomenon of obesity will persist to plague us with increasing ill-health and dismay. The issue is truly moral, not in an arbitrary man-made sense, but because under the law of karma (action and reaction on a mental and moral plane) every individual ultimately receives exactly as he has given. All that comes has been in some way deserved, but at least he can be assured of gaining the good he has fairly earned. "As ye sow, so shall ye reap."

The result of this faith in nature's primary law should not be fatalistic acceptance of existing circumstances, but joy in the knowledge that there is always something to be done about yourself. Any investment made will ultimately be paid back with interest. It is not the belief in karma which is fatalistic, as much as the belief in nothing, in no moral order or justice at all. The miasma of hopelessness and helplessness which undermines the efforts of many overweight persons to reduce, can be attributed more to the lack of a sense of meaning in their lives than to not caring how they look. Most of them are fundamentally loving, outgoing, useful human beings but are in some way unsure of their ability to determine the shape of their own destinies.

Power to control from within is the mark of maturity. As we grow older we must take increasing responsibility for the way the body looks and feels. The first child-body is a gift from God and parents. It is solicitously fed, loved and instructed. It expands with ease and thoughtless grace. Children are beautiful without even trying. They need not earn but only use what is given for their needs.

Later on we must strive consciously to wrest what we require from a less than friendly world. We must struggle to earn the love and admiration we still crave and find our rightful work without being told. We have to make an effort simply to be ourselves. Similarly we must deliberately assert mastery over our own bodies, and this challenge grows greater with each passing year. As children we anticipate "growing up" as a happy conclusion to our days of dependency. But if in growing up we do not continue to mature in willing acceptance of responsibility for what we become, then we end up far more helpless than children who at least *want* to develop and mature into something better.

This emphasis on the need to be forever re-creating ourselves does not imply any unrealistic endeavor to change our fundamental body design or traits of character. The outer structure is genetically determined, as are the walls of a house by the builder's blueprints. But that house can be barren or furnished, cluttered or clean, cold or warm, dark or glowing, according to the will of the occupant. That is what makes all the difference.

All individuals must, to some extent, remain at the mercy of parental attitudes, environment, glandular secretions and innate predispositions over which there can be but little control. In contradistinction to this aggregate of influences which *forms* the self from without, is that spirit which perpetually *transforms* from within. This is the miracle of man. He is the only creature capable of transcending himself.

Unlike the species of animals shaped over millenia by necessity for survival, man can do something more than merely survive and reproduce his kind. Just as he has hands to shape his environment, so he can take himself in hand and remake his destiny. He has the choice to choose or not to choose. In him there exists a power that forever makes all things new, and makes him capable of renewing himself. To effect the release of this transforming power is his first and final fulfillment.

2

The Lazy Man's Diet

WE HAVE CALLED THIS THE LAZY MAN'S DIET not to fool anyone into thinking it is going to be easy, but rather in the hope
that by understanding the basic issues involved we can be
spared the misery and frustration of unrealistic efforts to
reduce. The successful dieter must be too lazy to endure the
pains of futile endeavor, and above all, too lazy to struggle
on under the burden of excess weight.

The heaviest load the habitual overeater carries is not pounds
but pretense. He becomes, therefore, a target for any diet plan
which sets out to convince him that it is possible to get something for nothing. Actually the formula is reversed since what
is wanted is nothing in pounds for something in food. It still
doesn't balance any better, and neither do the scales. What
eventuates is nature's revenge — the feeling of having eaten
practically nothing and still having something left over on
hips and stomach.

The pathetic part is that unworkable diets represent a fruitless form of cheating on nature. The evidence of obesity
remains all too visible in the mirror and on the scales. Diet
fads spring from the same unrealism that deludes the hapless
sufferer into believing that it is possible to change his outer
configuration without some corresponding refiguring of his
fundamental attitudes. What needs to be shed is illusions.
Pounds will peel off after them.

The first illusion to dispel is the fear that the situation is hopeless, that try as one will there is nothing to be done. It *is* possible to be slender and each new day presents an opportunity to make a fresh start in that direction. Look at all the thin people there are in the world, and not all of them are remarkably intelligent, youthful or strong-minded. Never was a case for the affirmative better documented.

We suggest that you begin here and now to determine that you, too, are going to enjoy your inalienable right to live inside an efficient body uncluttered by excess baggage. Decide that you are just too busy with worthwhile interests and projects to waste time in anxious thoughts of inadequacy or failure. You *will* win out and that is that.

This initial resolve immediately raises the question, what diet plan? Some sort of strategem is, of course, necessary. It is well known that almost any diet will work to the extent that the dieter works at it. Yet virtually every scheme falls short of inspiring lasting success. We must find the reason why.

All reducing diets in some way reduce food intake. Some which stress high protein and low carbohydrate content have already become a way of life for large numbers of people. Every weight-watcher well knows that starchy foods are out. In spite of exaggerated claims which caused the "calories don't count" system to fall into disrepute, diets allowing fat intake have been somewhat exonerated, since small quantities of fat consumed at intervals do enable the body to burn its stored reserves and keep nerve tissue healthy.

Drinking diets allowing more than a minimal quantity of alcohol have the least to be said in their favor, though one which suggests a glass of champagne with each miniscule meal, including breakfast, at least points up the fact that, for most people, food has to serve as more than patch-work for the body.

Strict adherence to a pre-planned menu seems to work well enough for the slender who merely wish to stay in shape. For the seriously overweight person, however, all such deliberately contrived diet formulae have one built-in fallacy and this accounts for the fact that they rarely help those most in need.

The problem is that relying on cut-and-dried lists of forbidden versus non-forbidden items, each meticulously tabulated as to number and kind of calories, is never going to solve the problem of the food-dependent person. Rather it gives him one more prop to depend on.

What is needed is not a crutch to bear the weight but strength to reduce the load. It is not what is eaten that makes the difference, but our whole attitude toward food. Deciding what to eat should never become such a complicated, time-consuming nuisance that it distracts from the basic issue of why we are eating. Too much thought of food can, in the end, only arouse the appetite.

Fundamentally our plan is not just to make abstaining easier but to make the abstainer stronger. The point to be emphasized is not so much the selection of what is permissible to eat, but what food means in the economy of the entire personality. We must think in terms of permanent benefit and continuing improvement rather than of quick or spectacular changes in bodily dimensions.

Too many "low-cal" or "no-cal" methods try to trick the stomach into believing it has eaten more than it has, when results show it is really only the mind which is taken in by the game. The body is more realistic, yet it, too, can be confused and made to forget its basic instincts by the illusion-producing mind. An example of the way thought controls our involuntary reflexes is found in the research of psychologist Allen L. Seltzer who discovered that the dilation or contraction of the pupils reflects a person's true feelings about objects presented to the field of vision. The pupils of an individual who has just eaten will make no response to pictures of food. But if that same individual is hypnotized and told that he is hungry, his pupils will dilate markedly at the sight of the same pictures. Low-calorie products may, therefore, be of some value if they can hypnotize the mind into telling the body it is satisfied, but it is doubtful if this system will work in the long run because sooner or later the body catches on to the hoax. In some ways we are smarter than we think.

Compulsive overeating is caused mainly by our state of mind. This can be demonstrated by the fact that animals seldom grow fat, even when old. The less mind they have the less they deviate from their natural instinct to eat only what the body requires and can assimilate. Only animals under the influence of man are prone to eat the wrong foods or suffer from obesity.

What we propose is a way of dealing honestly with ourselves, not just because it is too much bother to keep on fabricating the daily rationalizations that accompany overeating, but because if hunger can be eliminated from the mind, the body will not unnecessarily mobilize its appetite-provoking mechanism. The first step is to find out what part of our hunger is legitimate, and reflects a genuine physical need, and what part is due to emotional or neurotic craving.

To accomplish this purpose we are presenting a ten point program of guiding principles. These are not just rules for eating, since each one demands the kind of thoughtful consideration that necessitates cooperation between the estranged body and mind. As in all attempts at reconciliation we must commence by opening lines of communication. When people fail to listen or hear one another, it is usually not for lack of shouting, but because they are preoccupied with acting out roles. They behave according to abstract or preconceived ideas instead of directly experiencing the particular situation and responding to its unique requirements.

So we must, for a while at least, put aside the rules, the role or routine and ask our body directly what *it* feels or would like. It is as logical to suppose that different people require different diets as to suppose that they have varying tastes in clothes, entertainment and religion. It is not just a question of habit. Bodies diverse in shape, color and age are bound to crave foods that supply their special needs. Overweight people are particularly prone to metabolic imbalance requiring the addition of certain nutriments and the elimination of others they are unable to assimilate and which, therefore, turn to fat. But how to find out what each must have when each one is unique? For this we must consult the final authority, the body itself. Since the organism can heal itself it can also diagnose with a wisdom beyond that of any physician. Our function is to heed what it tries to tell us.

1. *Indulge in frequent snacks. Eat a little, often, so that the stomach is never completely full or empty.*

The first thing to discover is what the physical part of us (not the mind) considers its minimal demand. By nibbling we eat only when honest hunger strikes. We respond to real physiological signals rather than to time registered on a clock or to childhood custom. In ministering to genuine appetite we become sensitive, not just to the need for food, but to the importance of showing courtesy and respect to the body which serves us so dutifully.

What we are doing is giving ourselves the same kind of "demand feeding" that psychologists now know keeps infants from becoming psychologically knotted up. Thus we return to the matrix from which our eating pattern originated, to begin untangling the complex skein of causes which have led to the present imbalance.

Nibbling keeps the stomach from shrinking or expanding unduly. The best way of eating is to consume the least amount of food that will satisfy. For a while you may not be able to trust your instincts in this respect, so eat a tiny bit and wait. Tell yourself that if you are still hungry you can have another few bites in a little while. Be reassured. The situation is analogous to that of a premature baby who can take only a few drops of milk at a time and must be attended to constantly. It is worthwhile to take the extra trouble, because the stage eventually passes. Gradually the body learns to be more patient and trusting and to wait a fair period before demanding the next feeding. It is always better not to wait too long for if the need can be anticipated the body does not lose faith and suddenly panic.

Another reason for trying to even out the flow of nourishment passing through the system is that hunger is not regulated by a sense of fullness in the stomach, as much as by the appe-stat located in the central region of the hypothalamus in the middle of your brain. (This shows what a central concern hunger can be!) Appestats work about the same way as the thermostat in your living room. They measure the glucose in your blood and keep the hunger level high enough to insure adequate blood sugar. The trouble is that it takes about half an hour after a meal for the glucose to be absorbed into the bloodstream and the signal to get back to you that hunger is satisfied. Meanwhile you may have been eating unnecessarily, simply because of this time lag. With controlled snacking this can not happen.

It is also possible for the appestat to be set too high, espe-cially if its sensitive balance is disturbed by erratic gorging. Then you must deliberately take measures to set it lower, as in turning down a thermostat.

Nibbling also prevents you from becoming so ravenous that you lose control and go on a binge. Allowing yourself to get into a state of nervous tension sets up a chain reaction of nega-tive responses which become increasingly hard to stop. Even a strong-willed person can be swept away by this irrational hunger-panic which cries out that the body's legitimate needs have been too long disregarded. It is better to know and allow for points of vulnerability. The problem for many fat people is not that they indulge themselves but that they make their body an enemy by neglecting real hunger when it manifests itself. For this reason stringent diets allowing no between-meal reassurance may do more harm than good.

Psychological studies have shown that children who are under-disciplined and children who are over-disciplined are both likely to succeed in life, if there is basic parental love and concern. The children who break down and fall to pieces are those treated *inconsistently,* first pampered, then punished, without ever really knowing the reason why. In brainwashing, the same technique of capriciously alternating solicitous and vindictive treatment quickly reduces the victim to abject sur-render or disorients him completely. The body, too, subjected to alternate feasts and famines, finally loses all sense of proportion and can no longer maintain its equilibrium.

A good time for a snack is an hour or so before a meal — especially if the meal is likely to be heavy. An appeaser such as a tall, hot drink (preferably not coffee or alcohol) with some sweetening in it will go a long way toward tempering the tantrums of an unruly appetite. Fruit and fruit juices are satisfactory pacifiers since their natural sugar content sends the appestat up. White sugar contains only empty calories and actually depletes the amount of vitamin B in the system, so try instead to sweeten your disposition with honey, molasses, raw or brown sugar.

Spacing calorie consumption evenly throughout the day helps the organism utilize its fuel more efficiently. Nourishment is transformed directly into energy instead of being stored away as fat, which may then be hard to bring back out of storage. Groups of animals fed only twice a day grew fat, while their companions who were allowed to nibble at will throughout the day ate an equal amount without gaining. The same applies to people. Yet Americans eat eighty percent of their food in the evening.

The main thing is not to become like an acquaintance of ours who would walk into an eating establishment, look at the menu, and say to the waiter, "I'll take this page." Incidentally he weighed over six hundred pounds and died at the age of thirty-five. Guess where he died. Where else but in a restaurant!

2. Cater to foods that strike your fancy or your mood.

This is really an extension of rule number one and works for essentially the same reasons. Experiments with babies just able to sit up have proven that if the infant is presented with an assortment of foods and allowed to take anything he pleases, he will in the end pick a nutritionally balanced diet. For a while he may go on a strained beet or applesauce jag but ultimately he selects what is best for him.

Many adults seem to lack the common sense the baby shows. Perhaps when they were young their instincts were seldom allowed to be trusted, so they never developed confidence in themselves. Strict diets clipped from magazines or books do little to restore the ancient wisdom of the cells which makes them genuinely want what is needed. Only when innate desires have been too often over-ridden do they lose their normal cravings and abdicate responsibility to the intellect, which relies on arbitrary formulae. Smoking, drinking, drugs, excessive salt and seasonings can compound the confusion by disguising harmful substances and training the taste to desire what the body does not require.

For many people the dinner hour is sacrosanct, but that still leaves the rest of the day to follow one's fancy. It may then turn out that dinner, too, can be subtly modified without anyone really noticing or caring. Most people are remarkably unobservant of what others are eating. Fill a large soup bowl with broth or consommé and dip it up with a teaspoon, or pick away at a salad. Concentrate on the conversation and, if no issue is made, few will notice how little has been consumed.

Try to eat like the babies mentioned above and keep a wide variety of snacking foods on hand. Your refrigerator should contain many kinds of cheeses and spreads to add to thin-sliced dark bread or crackers. Cottage cheese makes a satisfying base for fruit or raw vegetables. Yogurt topped with honey or mixed with frozen berries substitutes for ice cream. Keep such vegetables as celery, carrots and cauliflower, cut up raw, to chew on at a moment's notice, and add them to soups and casseroles. Salad ingredients and hard-boiled eggs should always be on hand, along with a variety of fresh fruits. Apples are particularly beneficial, not just because they are plentiful, cheap and nutritious, but also because they contain a tranquilizing element. None of these foods need much cooking or elaborate preparation, yet they are best for you.

We suggest that you keep a wide variety of soup mixes and preparations for hot and cold drinks on your shelves as well as raisins, unsalted nuts, coconut, dates, figs and other items that can be carried in a purse or briefcase or slipped into an office drawer. A visit to a health-food store will suggest dozens of other possibilities such as sunflower and pumpkin seeds, sesame bars and soybean products.

Now when you are hungry, survey your domain. Ask yourself which of the delicacies on hand would please you most. What does the appetite really crave? (Too often people go on eating unnecessarily, simply because they are not obtaining what they specifically need.) Nibble a little but save some for later, so as to have something to anticipate. If you know you may have another treat in an hour, you will feel less compulsion to eat so much at one time, and the hour may lengthen into two before you think of food again.

Whenever possible cater to your whims until you have an idea of what diet your body, which is like no one else's, prefers. Given this basic trust it will eventually reward you by good behavior and sharpened discrimination. This self-permissiveness is not the same as being disorganized. It is not a rejection of rule or routine but of *dependence* on custom for its own sake. The object is to become attuned to your body's innate rhythm and requirements. Once these are established they can be adjusted to meet the demands of convention.

3. Become a gourmet.

Experiment with new foods and unusual ways of preparing and serving them, to achieve a satisfaction that substitutes for sheer bulk. This is not to suggest that you should give more time to cooking. Seek out time-saving ideas, such as making unusual combinations of foods that eliminate the need for rich gravies and sauces. Once you have a well stocked larder, you can do less planning ahead and try new combinations of what happens to be on hand according to the inspiration of the moment. Think in terms of what would taste right and look inviting, rather than of the standard meat, starch and vegetable regimen. Food, too, needs to be loved for itself alone.

The same system can be followed at the store. Allow latitude for buying fruits and vegetables that are in season or that appear freshest, even if you don't customarily use them. As often as possible try to find some item you would not ordinarily prepare. Daring to experiment with herbs and spices not only makes gourmet delights out of cheap vegetables and grains (which are often the most nutritious) but testifies to the creativeness of your cooking. How many spices have you in your culinary vocabulary? What style do you set with nuts, mushrooms, parsley, etc.?

Above all give some thought to the so-called health foods such as yogurt, wheat germ, soybeans, sesame seeds and whole grain breads and cereals. Then if, after fair trial, you still don't care for them, you have earned the right to belittle, not before. If it takes a while to acquire the knack of combining them in taste-tempting ways, consider how much time you are saving with good health. Educating your appetite is as worthy of attention as educating your mind.

Some mothers develop a martyr complex about cooking. Often the planning of meals becomes a veritable obsession. If the kitchen is inviting and nobody is fussing around in it, however, children will soon learn to create their own imaginative mixtures, not only saving adults work, but gaining valuable training in self-sufficiency and originality. Spontaneity and daring in preparing meals can become such a pleasure that the eating turns out to be incidental.

The needs of the human body, and especially those of the hormone-producing endocrine system, are so varied and complex that nature has obligingly produced a dazzling variety of foods to insure complete nutrition. Why not take advantage of this abundance? An article in the April 1966 issue of *Pageant* magazine named eight special foods which reputable physicians report have the effect of contributing to sexual vigor, because they contain assimilable quantities of such essential minerals as zinc, magnesium, potassium, and phosphorous, as well as vitamins and amino acids. The foods listed are sesame seeds, honey, oysters, snails, nuts, buckwheat, beer, and wheat-germ oil.

These are, of course, given as supplements to an already balanced diet rich in milk and dairy products, since the sexual urge requires a general background of physical well-being. Milk has the distinction of being the highest grade protein known to man, the most easily absorbed and fully utilized. We notice that practically every one of the above listed substances, now vindicated by science, ranks as an exotic or gourmet food and has in folklore been ascribed special powers. Beer, for example, long prescribed for nursing mothers, is a rich natural source of estrogens. The women of ancient Babylonia believed that boiling sesame seeds and honey together was a recipe for romance. Sesame seed is rich in potassium and magnesium, and honey is a source of aspartic acid. Boiled together they produce the same potassium and magnesium salts of aspartic acid now being given by some doctors to women suffering from the "housewife syndrome"—a chronic state of fatigue and lethargy in relation to both housework and lovemaking. And, of course, we all know about Frenchmen and snails! But who would have thought that the lowly snail should turn out to be the only known food containing pure glycogen, an important element in the manufacture of male seminal fluid?

Consider your need for proper equipment as a shortcut to gourmet cooking. Steamers, infrared broilers, electric frying pans, blenders, juicers and cutters of all varieties are small investments affording lifetime dividends. Their special appeal lies in the allure they bestow on common victuals. We were impressed with this while visiting a summer camp for yoga students during its first season. In spite of the fact that the diet was strictly vegetarian and the budget stringent, rich and delicious soups were served daily. The cook, who was actually an unmarried librarian with no previous culinary experience and who had volunteered her services, refused to divulge the magic recipe for those marvelous soups about which everyone was so enthusiastic. Finally, to her embarrassment, the secret leaked out. She was simply taking all the leftovers from the previous day, including the breakfast porridge, combining them in the blender, and making this the base for the new soup.

4. Make a study of nutrition.

Health-food stores and libraries are sources of literature on nutrition which is not only educational but makes fascinating reading. Such excellent books as those by Adelle Davis and Gaylord Hauser render it unnecessary for us to dwell upon the merits of specific foods. The most important point is to know what to eliminate. Bleached white breads, starchy pastries, an excess of fried, canned, chemically embalmed foods, salt, white sugar and alcohol can go. It is a fallacy to cut out foods such as cheese and nuts because they are said to be fattening. Just space them out, nibbling a minute quantity every few hours, and they will help your body burn its own excess fat. You can eat less of these foods because they afford greater satisfaction. If the food is wholesome, it can be assimilated and converted into energy. It is the devitalized substances which are unusable and clog arteries, pores and organs. The message any health-food expert would brand in your brain is this: The less your food has been tampered with by man, the better it will be for you.

We suggest serious consideration of the whole concept of eating meat. The fact that many people are shocked by the idea of living without meat shows how hard it is to think objectively about food and how closely bound it is to our whole approach to life. Nevertheless challenging arguments can be raised in favor of the vegetarian or modified vegetarian regime. We will shy away from the moral issue of whether our lot can be bettered by causing pain although it is hard to be convinced that it does not hurt to die, even for an animal. This is a question each individual must answer to the satisfaction of his own conscience. Nor is it our place to forward the argument that vegetarianism produces a more refined, psychically sensitive body. Moral and esthetic reasons aside, for the sake of our health, we must reexamine our position on eating animals.

From time immemorial meat was supposed to make men masculine. Now the situation has changed. According to doctors with whom we have talked, and who are quite concerned about the subject, the estrogen and hormonal substances given animals to increase their appetites and tenderize them for slaughter, are being transmitted to the men who devour them, and are exerting a feminizing influence.

Mark Douglas tried unsuccessfully to lose weight for several years, but shed fifty pounds when he ceased to eat meat, and found his previously ravenous appetite diminishing along with his waistline. This discovery led us to pay attention to mounting evidence that artificially castrating animals to induce them to overeat, inclines those who consume their flesh to eat more also. Since meat is a stimulant it may give the illusion of satisfaction, but it will make you hungrier sooner. Like pouring oil on a fire, meat-eating results in a quick flare-up of energy, but is not conducive to sustained activity or feats of endurance.

Flesh foods are seldom fresh foods. Cured to begin with, until softened by decomposition, they are a fertile breeding ground for germs of disease. Meat also contains poisonous wastes such as uric acid, urea, and creatine, which the animal would have excreted. The bloodstream and kidneys of the meat-eater must take on the extra burden and strain to eliminate them. The uric acid in meat has been linked to arthritis and unassimilable animal fats are known to cause deposits of cholesterol in the arteries, thereby impairing circulation. Heart attacks and cancer are far less prevalent among vegetarian people, animals and nations. Dr. Robert Yerkek of Yale reports finding not one case of malignancy in any of the hundreds of chimpanzees he has examined.

It can also be pointed out that the swiftest animals such as the gazelle, the largest and smartest such as the elephant, those closest to man such as apes, chimpanzees and gorillas, the strongest and most enduring such as the ox and the horse, are grain or fruit eaters. Human beings themselves consume only the grain-fed animals, not dogs, cats or rats. Eating meat is a peculiar form of discrimination because carnivorous people eat only vegetarian animals. Meat-eating animals have pointed teeth while the teeth of grain chewers tend to be flat. The teeth of men are more flat than pointed.

Many dieters have found it advisable to reduce their dependence on animal flesh gradually. (The same person who gets fat is often the very one who appears most horrified at the thought of doing without meat.) They graciously accept what is served when dining out, but at home rely on fish, cheese, eggs, avocados, dairy products, soybeans, lentils, nuts and grains to supplement the customary vegetables and fruits. Once liberated from the habit of making meat the focal point of every meal, they can enhance their appreciation of other nutritious foods.

Seafood makes a good compromise, being an almost ideal source of protein. Meat has been tampered with by man, but most fish live in a nutritionally perfect environment, enabling them to absorb many minerals which the water holds in solution, particularly phosphorous which the human brain specially requires. This lends credence to the old adage that fish is brain food. Fish is usually cheap and plentiful and can be cooked in a variety of delicious ways.

In general, fish is preferable to poultry which in turn is preferable to lamb and veal, and these are better than pork and beef products.

Look into the case for vegetarianism. The strongest evidence is presented by the vegetarians themselves. Some are fat or sickly, just as anyone else can be, but on the whole they endure to a vigorous old age, have good figures, and are pleased (as are the writers of this book) to speak of the advantages of their way of life. Becoming a vegetarian is an exercise in thinking for yourself rather than relying on conventional opinion.

5. Review your smoking and drinking habits.

Smoking and drinking are suspect because they interfere with your body's natural functions. Of the two, smoking is often the worse culprit because it introduces alien and poisonous substances into your body, polluting the breath of life at its very source. It is estimated that the total absorbing surface of the lungs is six hundred square feet, or about twenty-five times the surface area of the skin. This delicate membrane is the crucial borderline between oxygen which technically is external to the body, and that which is internal and part of you. Smoking's "instant smog" clogs and congests the cell walls right at this essential point of entrance.

Heavy smokers, for all their insistence that the habit cuts appetite, are as likely to have weight problems as anyone else, unless or until they have so damaged themselves, that they fall prey to emphysema, heart disease or cancer. In these cases they may become too thin. The ill effects of smoking are manifest in the humiliation of being an addict psychologically dependent upon a habit known to be expensive and destructive. Smoking shows a basic irreverence for the miracle of the body, the penalty being that smokers die younger and often of peculiarly ugly diseases. The dulling of awareness is also shown by the extraordinary inability of many smokers to realize or care how obnoxious their habit is to others, whose atmosphere they fill with miasmic fumes. This is particularly true of mothers, who instill the addiction into their young children. Babies born to women who smoke are on the average smaller and, when nursing, can become quite ill from the poisonous effects of the nicotine in their mother's milk.

Asking "Do you mind if I smoke?" seldom helps, since few people will speak out and say, "Yes, I do mind." The smoker's psychic membrane of sensitivity to other's feelings seems to thicken and darken along with the tissue of the lungs until he is unaware of the ashes, butts and scorches left in his wake.

Many smokers are more oriented to the illusive world of advertising that to the reality of people's reactions. A woman well-known to us, whose husband smoked three packs a day, was in tears every night because he constantly criticized her inability to season food in the manner his mother had used. Although his life was entirely sedentary he was thoroughly imbued with the idea that lighting up a cigarette made him a rugged "he-man" type. She is now happily married to a nonsmoker who enthusiastically proclaims her to be a wonderful cook.

The illogic of the smoking habit is typified by the case of a friend of ours who is fanatically obsessed with keeping her house and children constantly scrubbed clean. Yet her husband, a nonsmoker, once admitted in confidence that he could not bear to kiss her because her breath reeked with the stench of tobacco. He really would rather have been faithful to her, he admitted in the same conversation, but. . . . Possibly she believes that using every soap and detergent sold in the market excuses her from being dirty on the inside.

As long as men have doubts of their masculinity, smoking will continue to provide them with reassurance, while giving them a comforting object upon which to suck. Women, too, can prove their ability to be like men as they manipulate the supremely symbolic cigarette.

Starting on a diet may not be the best time to shed the smoking habit, but neither should it be the occasion to replace reliance on food with a more helpless reliance on smoking. Some people take a new dietary regime as a signal to switch to black coffee and cigarettes. They end up in a state of nerves and then blame lack of food for the ravages of their new dependencies. Subconsciously they may not really want to succeed, and the wrecking of their system provides an excuse for discontinuing their diet.

One point on which most ex-smokers agree is that the addiction must be kicked outright without tapering off, and tobacco products kept as much as possible out of sight. Some substitute pleasure should be found. The most effective distraction for any kind of oral dependency is a love affair, but for those restricted in amorous pursuits, deep breathing exercises are recommended. Since smoking involves the mouth and the act of breathing, learning to make respiration a conscious art, instead of an unthinking dulling of the senses, goes to the physiological roots of the problem.

A student of ours reported that she liked to smoke because it made her feel like a volcano. She had a strong pressure to erupt and let out the smouldering resentments within, and to date all her very real efforts to give up the habit have failed. Other students had fallen into habits of improper breathing, and lighting up a cigarette was the only way they knew to inhale from the depths and let the air out slowly and completely. In cases such as these, breathing exercises, with their emotionally tranquilizing and physically regularizing effects, prove remarkably helpful.

Since smoking disrupts the rhythm of breathing, we recommend that it be supplanted by the Alternate Breathing exercise outlined in our chapter, *Breath, The Rhythm of Being Alive.* Deep breathing should be accompanied by mental visualization of your entire body being nourished and replenished by the surrounding atmosphere.

Controlled respiration has proven effective in overcoming the craving for a smoke because it demands willingness to take action. There is not just the mouthing of statements to the effect that the smoker realizes it is a bad habit and would like to give it up. Part of the lip game of smoking is that protestations of the desire to quit seldom mean much, but provide one more channel for the dissipation of energy.

In discussing these issues of eating meat, smoking and drinking, we find ourselves in a position reminiscent of the country parson who was preaching fervently against all the sins ranging from murder to crap-shooting. In her pew a devout old lady rocked and swayed intoning "Amen, Amen." Then the parson started in on the subject of snuff-dipping. The old lady sat bolt upright and muttered, "Now he done stopped preachin' and took to meddlin'."

The need is not to judge but to clarify the issues involved with regard to the place of these substances in the diet of anyone aspiring toward health, vitality and enthusiasm for living. Many people smoke and drink to excess because they wish to destroy themselves or others, and that is another problem out of our domain.

Alcohol raises a different issue, because even though it is a more "natural" substance than tar and nicotine, being produced by the body itself, it can and does lead to greater heartbreak and suffering. We don't have much regard for drinking, not because we are anti-alcohol, but because we are anti-calorie. Alcohol changes into saturated fat and people with abnormally high blood fat and cholesterol have been discovered to be gaining almost twice the number of calories from alcohol as those considered normal. The nemesis of many dieters is the cocktail hour with accompanying appetizers. Enough cocktail hours spread over enough years provide a sure guarantee that the drinker will no longer greatly care what sort of figure he has, and inevitably he regains the pot-belly of his bottle-fed infancy.

We do not suggest giving up this sacrosanct institution, but only that it be continued with one slight difference, which is to change it into the oxygen cocktail hour. Fifteen minutes of deep breathing with leg raising, slow stretching, bending and tensing positions will invigorate you to the point where that first drink may scarcely be wanted. Fill to capacity—but with air. Overbreathing may result in a sensation of being high, but without the hangover.

Many executives report licking the alcohol-calorie menace by setting the dinner hour at an earlier time. Busy people find that a promptly served supper leaves them with time for an evening of creative relaxation, and *after* a meal there is seldom the same craving for a drink.

Relaxation purchased with pills, alcohol or cigarettes is like money borrowed from the bank. Sooner or later it must be paid back in kind, along with interest payments of disturbed sleep, medical bills, and inefficiency. The oxygen cocktail hour is like putting money in the bank. Energy reserves will be available in time of need and pay a continuing dividend in health. The cash saved from liquor purchases can be diverted into finer pleasures. In the United States more money is spent on liquor than on education. A person who reverses this trend is, by that decision, becoming fit to lead rather than follow the herd. The excuse that "Everybody does it" no longer overrides the quiet question, "Is this what I really want?"

6. Fill up with non-caloric bulk-producing foods.

Few dieters take sufficient advantage of the delightful fact that certain foods such as celery, cabbage and tomatoes can be eaten without weight gain. More calories are used in digesting them than are found in the foods themselves, leaving a balance in favor of the dieter. One reason why calorie-counting is outmoded is that it fails to take account of the metabolic cost of digestion. Ninety calories of sugar or starch dissolve right into fat, whereas the same number in the form of fish or a hard-boiled egg, stimulate glandular action and speed metabolism, even to the point of burning more calories than have been consumed.

Well-to-do people are apt to be slender, simply because they can afford expensive proteins and take the trouble to obtain salads, fruits and vegetables. A high-protein diet alone is not the answer, particularly if based on inordinate amounts of meat. Other foods provide many of the vitamins and minerals needed to form the enzymes which accomplish the actual work of burning fat and converting it into energy. Effort is also expended in the chewing and sorting out processes within the digestive tract. For example, more calories are required to digest a whole orange, eaten pulp and all, than to drink the juice, and so fewer calories remain to be stored. The fiber in bulky foods also supports the growth of valuable intestinal bacteria and increases the amount of vitamin B in the system. Animals fed on smooth food alone do not thrive. Even the addition of filter paper gives them the roughage necessary for proper digestion.

Scientists are now working on methods of adding cellulose to food, in order to create the illusion of more substance with fewer calories. Whether this will aid the dieter is questionable, since rats fed on this diluted product simply increased their intake until they were receiving their normal nutritional quota. One would think that human organisms would be as intelligent as rats in gauging their requirements. The answer may still lie in doing it the natural way, even as the main developer of cellulose additives, Dr. O. A. Battista, indicates in the following statement quoted in the book, *The Overweight Society*, by Peter Wyden:

"Liquid diets aren't satisfying! You've got to diet the natural way, and cellulose is the natural way. You've got to fill those intestines! Now a vegetarian increases his cellulose intake drastically. He probably triples it over the rest of us, and he's probably the healthiest fellow there is. We've done nothing to the microcrystals of cellulose. We've just unhinged them. They're just as nature made them."

A comedian once remarked, "You can eat all the food you want and stay thin — you just don't swallow it." A more workable alternative would seem to be to eat all you want, but of those foods which leave no calories behind.

7. Refresh your system with plenty of liquids.

The human body, like the surface of the earth, contains mostly water. Water is the great purifier. Yet many dieters, just at that time when the body needs extra water to wash away wastes, cut down its cleansing flow for the sake of a pound or two of loss registered on the scales. A better system would be to reduce salt intake and substitute herbs and spices so that the body will not hold excess fluid.

Many people who have no time for special diets have found that switching to the new "no-cal" drinks does wonders for the waistline. This may be because drinking doesn't seem like eating, so it is easy to underestimate how many calories liquids are adding to your daily allowance. A chubby teen-ager recently confided, "I'm on a fast." All she was taking was milk — three quarts a day.

Bouillon cubes, thin soups, tomato juice, diluted chocolate-type drinks, decaffeinated coffee, herbal and exotic teas provide sufficient variety to indulge in endless experimentation. Many people are surprised to discover that coffee may be pleasantly varied with maple syrup, brown sugar or molasses instead of white sugar. Numerous movie stars have come to consider their blenders second in importance only to their press agents, and rival one another in whipping up frothy concoctions of juices, fruits, vegetables, cottage cheese, yogurt and eggnogs, in combinations that stagger the imagination.

A real advantage of the liquid mixtures is that they can be sipped by the hour. During a prolonged meal they can be dipped up from a soup bowl a teaspoon at a time. A sense of extra nourishment can be imparted by serving them hot, and they can be diluted indefinitely. A tall glass or bowl of some unspecific appearing substance, gives the illusion of eating right along with others, at least until enough independence has been established to realize how little these "others" actually notice or care, as long as your appearance is relatively healthy. The compulsion to go along with the crowd is part of the basic problem, more often rationalization than requirement.

One way to cultivate the self-reliance which counters food-dependency, is to discover new drinks and learn to like them. A woman of our acquaintance laid in an enormous quantity of drinks and soup mixes at the time of the Cuban crisis. Then when war seemed less imminent, she was faced with the problem of their consumption. In the end, she became fond of almost every kind and still drinks a good proportion of her diet, much to her figure's advantage.

8. Insure yourself against worry with a daily vitamin.

A good multiple vitamin pill, taken daily, is a must for most adults. Even amateur nutritionists can not be sure that the food they have taken pains to select, has not been devitalized by chemical sprays and long-term storage. Vitamins are important, not just for their immediate benefits, but also for the cumulative effect of keeping your body in balance. In addition, they provide anxiety insurance. If the rest of your diet is reasonably complete and rich in protein, you can be assured that your requirements are being met as far as food intake goes.

You will still, however, need exercise, correct breathing, and good living habits to enable your system to assimilate all the good things you pour into it.

Supplements such as vitamin C (which the body can not store and needs every day) and wheat-germ oil (for heart and glandular action) seem to be helpful to many people. But extra vitamins must be handled with care, since they are meant to be balanced and taking one without its relatives may lead to serious difficulties. Children have been badly damaged by too much vitamin D and, from time to time, cases turn up of people turning quite yellow from overdoses of raw carrot juice. Although vitamin D has been called "the sunshine vitamin" by advertising men, the sun does not actually impart any vitamins. The sunlight brings about chemical changes within the cells of the skin and this releases a form of vitamin D into the system.

For most people the problem is not so much what to add to their diet as how to release the nutritive qualities of the food they are already consuming. Unless you suffer from some gross deficiency, fresh air, sunshine, and an active useful life can do more to invigorate you than any conceivable pill or elixir.

9. Plan your table strategy.

No matter how carefully you design your diet, there are going to be times when you are obliged to sit hungrily at the table with mounds of food tempting you and time to be thoroughly tempted. Advance planning can take the strain out of such occasions. Much of it can be easy such as putting the food at the other end of the table or leaving serving dishes in the kitchen. If you are the cook you may find that putting out a little less food than you think necessary results in serving the proper amount. Sometimes good intentions do actual harm, like the friendly monkey who, seeing a fish in the water, rushed to rescue it from drowning by carrying it up into a tree. Too many cooks kill with kindness, when the real favor would be to spare with sparsity. A mountain of unneeded food may be consumed, simply because "it is there."

Small games help set the pattern of restraint. Try waiting until everyone else begins, keep the conversation away from food, and sit back so that your face isn't hanging over the plate. While waiting to eat, practice the Stomach Press. Sit up straight with your back against the chair, feet flat on the floor, hands resting naturally on your lap. Exhale completely and pull your stomach in as far as you can, as though trying to press it against your backbone. Hold about ten seconds with the breath out. Aside from being an excellent exercise, this causes you to consider where the food is going and to question whether you require so generous a container for your daily bread.

Make it a point to slice your food into small portions, if you would similarly reduce your own proportions. Eat each separate piece slowly and chew thoroughly to allow time for the digestive juices in the mouth to act on the food properly. Concentrate on taste and texture. While you are digesting, visualize what you have eaten being transformed into energy which pervades your cells with radiant health. The use of the mind confirms your control over the body.

Don't be afraid to leave something on your plate. Much downright obesity is caused by mothers overloading their children's dishes and then insisting that every bit be eaten. Some people never escape the compulsion to avoid waste by "obeying mama" decades after she has left the scene. For most people it is necessary to end each meal feeling just a bit hungry. Accept this as one of the facts of life and with the patience to realize that the sense of satiety comes later after the meal. Food is in your mouth for seconds, in your stomach for hours, but around your waist for the rest of your life. So remember —eat it now, wear it later!

10. Fasting is more than fast.

If and when you seriously intend to start a diet, we advise beginning with a fast of one day. In the early stages, when the appetite is not yet under control, this is easier than enduring constant temptations. In fact, it saves you from having to think about food at all, and gives immediate results to encourage progress after initial enthusiasm has worn off. Those who have tried fasting are often amazed that this really can be the easiest way. Discovering that you have the fortitude to abstain makes a pleasant bonus.

Fasting may appear to contradict what we said earlier about snacking, but actually both systems can be combined. When not abstaining completely, follow the nibbling pattern.

Interestingly enough it is the overweight people, who could easily afford to fast, who are shocked by the idea of missing a few meals. Even if they can be prevailed upon to make the experiment they seem subconsciously determined to resist with weak or nervous spells. The reaction of these individuals to the idea of a fast is so out of proportion to the actual deprivation involved that one suspects something in them is already set against the idea of the new discipline. Fasting forces self-confrontation and an assessment of the will to succeed.

Fasting cleans out your whole system and effects a healing purge of body and mind. Animals know enough to cease eating when sick. People, too, can often throw off diseases by substituting water or thin liquids for food, allowing the body to withdraw its energies from digestion and throw all resources into the battle against invading germs. Some prefer a "beggar's fast" of water alone, while others settle for a "royal fast" allowing coffee, tea and fruit juices. A single day's fast can be the decisive step toward reorienting your whole pattern of eating.

There is an art to fasting. For one thing it should be meaningful. Let this be a time of general catching up and self-appraisal. Update correspondence, clean closets, garden, read a worthwhile book or help some needy person. It is easier to take a double discipline than to seek compensating distractions, though pleasures are not to be avoided if they come your way. You are doing a good thing by fasting, so why not accomplish something extra, that you may feel deservedly proud of your-self and in a mood to enter the long siege of dieting ahead.

Fasting is also therapeutic for those of normal weight who are not on a diet, and even the underweight have been known to gain after a short fast.

Some authorities recommend prolonged periods of noneat-ing continuing for days or even weeks, but in practice marathon fasts don't seem to make that much lasting difference. Extreme fasting has taken weight off people in spectacular style, but virtually every one ends up as heavy as before. The shock of such a disruption to the metabolic rhythm may even stiffen resistance to continued dieting.

We have found that the best system is to fast one day a week. Mondays are usually preferable, because this affords the opportunity to begin the week anew and compensate for week-end indulgences. You will probably be hungry part of the day, but no more than when you simply cut down on food. By Tuesday your appetite will have diminished and you can con-tinue on an extremely light diet. Most people gradually start eating more during the week, but before matters are out of control there is always another Monday and another chance. Even God is said to have rested on the seventh day of creation, so you, too, can take a holiday from eating.

It is important to exercise when fasting, so that your body can burn off accumulated toxins and bring the excess fat back out of storage. Also, it prevents you from sinking into a mental morass. Drink plenty of water even if you do so deliberately since there is a tendency not to feel thirsty without food. You may feel hungry, but when the urge to eat passes naturally, without appeasement, you will have learned an important lesson.

A fast of more than a day may require medical supervision, but to abstain throughout a single twenty-four hour period should be possible for any reasonably healthy individual. The fast should not be broken abruptly, but tapered off with light snacks, until your eating pattern is reestablished.

If a day of fasting seems inordinately difficult, then something must be askew physically or psychologically, and should be investigated. Perhaps the reaction will reveal a clue as to why there should be a weight problem in the first place. A weekly fasting period using the same day of the week whenever possible is the easiest, laziest way for many to maintain lasting control. We mention it at the end to emphasize that fasting may prove to be the cornerstone around which is built the foundation of the new you.

3

Streamlining Your Attitude

THE PHILOSOPHER, KIERKEGAARD, once described a man who was so abstracted from himself, that he never knew he was alive until one day he woke up and found himself dead. This ghostly limbo represents an ultimate stage in the involution of what psychologists describe as the oral character. Such a person focuses inordinate attention on the mouth and all modes of taking in, yet remains forever haunted by a benumbing sense of deprivation. He may be satiated but is never deeply satisfied. Indeed he never can be satisfied because, being out of touch with his own deeper nature, he never really knows what it is that he craves, and so must make do with substitutes.

Oral types may mask their overweening compulsion to ingest love, admiration, and solicitous concern by excessive protestations of care and concern for others, often members of their immediate families. Eventually this attention becomes suffocating to the objects of such pseudo-maternal devotion, who in one way or another refuse to serve as targets for the projection of another person's private neurosis. The oral character reacts to the inevitable rebuff by feeling himself insufficiently appreciated and by becoming depressed. Often he begins to eat or drink in compensation. He devours, not that he may work and love and grow, but simply for the sake of being fed.

The oral character's frequent conviction of having been victimized, may have been a reality at the start, justified by lack of tenderness and warmth in the early stages of infancy when he was most helpless and vulnerable. But it becomes increasingly delusive as his fixation at the child stage compels him to act out, again and again, his infantile frustrations and, when necessary, set the stage for their repetition. He seems as helpless to overcome his irrational behavior as was the baby to prevent the original hurt. His continuing sense of vulnerability is masked by rigid defensive attitudes, or with an armor of flesh, so that he may never know hunger again. Of course he soon craves more food or attention because the split in his personality makes a crack through which energy leaks away. At their most debilitating, such individuals are like psychic sieves, draining themselves and all who would pour love and care into them.

One way in which this condition of fixation at the earliest or oral level can be mitigated, is for an individual to go back into his personal history and try to recapture and relive his early experiences. This is the basis of modern psychoanalytic technique, and also comes strikingly close to echoing the Biblical injunction, that it is necessary to be born again to achieve the kingdom of heaven. The question is whether it is always necessary to seek out our origins in time in order to get back on the track. Could not improvement be obtained if we could somehow penetrate to the timeless core of our being, out of which we are forever renewed?

Because the oral person has been disappointed too early in life he is afraid to reach out. Yet there are needs he must satisfy and which he would like the adult world to attend to without effort on his part. His is the original "world owes me a living" syndrome. It did, at one stage, but he seems not to realize that the time has come for him to grow up. Weak in his aggressive drive, or backbone sense, he inverts his hostility into variants of the sucking, leeching, clinging, spitting and biting which served to allay his earliest demands. As before, he finds these methods fairly successful in getting what he wants. The irony is that the things obtained by these means can never satisfy. The prevalence of this attitude of supine clinging is epitomized in Oscar Wilde's remark that "the greatest tyranny in the world is that of the weak over the strong."

Oral people are often profuse talkers, pouring themselves out not just in a plethora of words but in a verbal style of thinking which tends toward looseness, abstraction, and loss of contact with the earth, ultimate source of all nourishment. A manic phase of grandiose speculation and endless conversation about future accomplishments frequently fades into depression and a drugged feeling of lethargy. The need to maintain self-esteem may be bolstered by the conviction of being an unrecognized genius. Some oral types do have genius and an uncommon precocity is typical, but more often the genius is for constructing dreams of glory.

These early developers among oral types sometimes seem like flowers nurtured in poor soil whose stalks have grown too high. They shoot up to become so long and reedy that when it comes time to bloom no energy remains for blossoming. They seem not to have their feet on the ground, to be out of touch, windy, in the clouds, or otherwise off the earth, with a corresponding lack of physical coordination.

Anyone who suspects himself of being an oral or mouth-centered person, can be assured of being in good company, since in many respects the whole of civilization has been tending in the direction of mouth worship ever since Eve gave Adam a piece of fruit to eat. Truly our first parents ate themselves out of house and home! Perhaps this legend refers symbolically to some sort of birth trauma occurring in the infancy of the race, with which we have been morbidly obsessed ever since?

A serious weight problem can be made to seem less a sneak attack from behind and below, if one can realize what it is that has antagonized these forces at the foundation of our being, cutting the mind off from the body, the flower of intellect from the root of instinct. It is not enough to recognize a predisposition to overcompensate the inner emptiness by seeking inordinate praise, love and admiration, and when these inevitably fail to try to make it up with food. One must understand that this is an attack not *by* but *on* the body, and the aggressors are one's confused desires.

The food-dependent person must first of all become aware of what he really wants or needs. This quest is confounded because he is surrounded by media which advertise bountifully bosomed girls and boundlessly delectable enticements to satisfy every appetite. Magazines and television spin out fantastic dreams and inane imitations of life to distract the multitudes. The diversion of desires is deliberate. It sells products. We find it mirrored in the chaos of sign-cluttered cities and competing countries.

The danger in not knowing what you want is illustrated in the oriental tale of the man who, on doing a favor for a certain god, was rewarded by a gift of three wishes. When he communicated this piece of good fortune to his wife she told him to ask first for riches. But he replied, "We both have very ugly noses that make people laugh at us. Let us first wish for beautiful straight noses." The wife insisted she wanted wealth first. Finally, incensed, the man exclaimed, "Let us both have beautiful noses and nothing but noses!" Instantly both of their bodies were covered with beautiful noses; but they looked so fantastic that both quickly agreed to wish a second time for their removal. This was done but they also lost their own noses and were left with none at all, looking uglier than before. They still wanted to have two beautiful noses but now feared to be questioned about their transformation lest they be regarded as fools who could not mend their circumstances, even with the help of three wishes. So both agreed to take back their ugly noses and be as they were originally. The moral of this story is that we must be careful about what we desire, because getting what we ask for can lead to the worst bondage of all.

There is love for food and there is lust for food. The former can be satisfied, but the latter never can because it is based not on real need but on the illusion that food can stand for something which it is not. The individual who would become cognizant of his own wants must be encouraged in the belief that his legitimate yearnings can be satisfied. For every problem there is some solution, but the two must be rightly matched. Solutions themselves are easy enough to find and oral people specialize in them. The problem is to find the problem. Once the issue has been clearly formulated it will vanish or spontaneously suggest its own solution. If not solvable in itself, it may be resolved into some larger context where it is seen as necessary for growth.

One such resolution is to look at our situation from another angle, seeing life not as a problem to be solved but as a reality to be experienced. If there is a problem, it is how to deepen the dimensions of our experience or how to relate our problem-solving activities more meaningfully to the issues at hand. Facile answers to our fundamental queries are everywhere, so plentiful in fact, that it seems as though there were more answers than questions, just as there are more products to satisfy our needs than needs to be satisfied. Perhaps these many answers have their uses, but only insofar as they lead us to ask again, "What is it that is lacking in me? How am I to be filled? From where is my strength to come, and what would I be like if I were strong?"

The following discussion deals not so much with food per se, as with attitudes about food. We begin with the first lesson in mouth control which, since we are concerned with inner factors, relates to the proper use of the tongue.

1. Don't talk about your intention to reshape your figure or refigure your shape.

For your own sake as well as that of your family and friends who probably wouldn't believe you anyway, let them discover for themselves the astounding fact that you mean business. Brush aside comments and compliments, letting figures speak for themselves. Determine to act with enlightened selfishness. Step number one in the unfooling process is to aim for improvement because you want to take pride in yourself, and not to elicit praise or admiration. All your best resolutions can be frittered away in wordy explanations that too easily substitute for the reality of results.

When you are at the problem-solving stage you may feel obliged to talk out your difficulties. With the deepening of your capacity to feel the new life stirring in the depths of yourself there is less to say and more to experience. The bee searching for a blossom buzzes loudly; but when he enters and sips its nectar, all is silence.

We have discovered that if you tell people you have lost thirty, forty, or more pounds and are approaching normal weight, they will usually exclaim, "Don't lose any more!" Usually they are registering surprise rather than anxiety. This admonition is the first thing that enters their heads and is their way of expressing care and concern. A friend told us how he had lost fifty pounds, bragged about it, and then gained back ten pounds in a week because his wife and friends began to fill him with fears that he might get *too* thin.

One phrase repeated first thing in the morning can serve as a reminder to talk less and love more. Say to yourself, "In quietness and in confidence may I find my strength for today." Then pause and meditate briefly on the power within.

2. Cultivate self-reliance.

The Indian saint, Ramakrishna, tells the story of two monks who were passing through a forest when a tiger approached them. One said, "There is no reason why we should flee; the Almighty will certainly protect us." Whereupon his companion replied, "No, brother, let us run away. Why should we trouble the Lord for what can be accomplished by our own exertions?"

One of the pitfalls in the fight to be free of fat is dependence on the opinions of friends and family, or even dependence on religion, if this prevents you from exerting your own will to be saved. Often, other people will try to keep you as you have always been because this is your role in life to them, and they, too, rely on the outer form of things. Much as they claim they are all for change and improvement, they may unconsciously try to thwart you. The same friend, mentioned above, told us that every time he informs his wife that he is on a diet, she obligingly produces a special dinner of fish, salad and fruit. The following night when he comes home really hungry, he finds an evening meal of spaghetti, hot-buttered garlic bread and chocolate-cream pie.

Most women believe that the way to a man's heart is through his stomach. Recently this truism has taken on ironic implications since it has been proven that excess weight accounts for many malfunctions of the circulatory system and is a major factor in the alarming statistic that of all deaths in the United States, fifty-five percent are due to heart disease. According to figures released by the Metropolitan Life Insurance Company, out of five million insured people, nearly half of all men and women over thirty years of age are twenty percent or more above their best weight — and insurance tables make generous allowances to begin with. At twenty-five pounds overweight, the mortality rate is twenty-five percent higher than average, while at fifty pounds over, the mortality rate jumps fifty to seventy-five percent higher than average. Population research financed by the Metrecal interests estimates that while there are about fifty-two million people in the United States who are conscious of having a weight problem, approximately twenty-seven million more are overweight but will not admit it, even to themselves. They calculated, therefore, that fifty-eight percent of all American adults suffer from some degree of obesity.

It is not necessary to take the word of statisticians. Stand on a city street corner watching the people pass and you may wonder if the situation has not been underestimated. Part of the problem is that the condition of being overweight is so common that it is easy to regard yourself as normal in comparison with your pudgy friends, instead of asking, "What is right for *me*?"

An obese person is an invalid crippled by fat. The strange thing about this sickness is that it evokes so little sympathy or recognition. It is so obvious, yet cruelly hidden behind the ludicrous disguise of excess flesh. The symptom is not the illness, any more than spots are measles. Beneath the pangs of hunger something is amiss. The individual still has to make up his mind to cease being destiny's dupe, and to act rather than react. Free will must be expressed as the will-to-be-free. He will find then, that miracles do happen, though it is necessary to work hard to bring them to pass.

3. Practice the rhythm method of girth control.

As you reduce in pounds you may feel like a geologist excavating successive layers of physical and mental resistances, exhuming long-buried complexes, frustrations and resentments. Some hardened strata will require extra digging, as you work through problems previously interred and effect their creative resolution in the light. Realize these setbacks are part of the process of delving into consciousness and a token of success in reaching your depths.

It is wise to consult a doctor if you feel unwell, but some battles must be fought out *alone* in order to prove to yourself your ability to endure and win through. Group therapy has its advantages but also serious limitations, as shown in the records of the national TOPS (Take Off Pounds Sensibly) movement. With more than sixty thousand members, the combined enthusiasm of the group has started a veritable avalanche of fat rolling off mountainously proportioned people. But even the broad experience of these "Eat Nix," "Waist Aways" and "Invisi-Belles" as they variously call themselves, has shown that the process soon reverses and the "Thick N'Tired" are soon as thick and tired as before, unless they can learn to stand alone — particularly at those times when everyone else is sitting together at the table. To the extent that they can fight for themselves, the war is won.

When, therefore, moments of weakness arise, try not to hate yourself for slipping away from the ideal. Just stop short of utter indulgence, even if it means eating two rather than three pieces of pie or foregoing half the whipped cream on a pudding. Any gesture that allows you to retain some shred of the old determination to make good, snatches victory from the jaws of defeat. Even in the midst of being vanquished by a Sunday dinner, you can allow one pea to remain intact on your plate, as a token of faith in tomorrow's new beginning.

All growth proceeds through cycles of ebb and flow and so it is natural that you will hit your highwater mark, retreat, and then prepare for a new resurgence. You can not step forward with both feet at once. Recognize this fact and allow for the rhythm of repeated forward thrusts, keeping your eyes on the goal ahead. Expecting and planning for this wavelike progress, will afford the fluidity to dissolve the brittle defensiveness of food dependency. It allows latitude for the wide swings of mood to which oral types of personality are notoriously prone, ranging from euphoric ego inflation to abject depression. (One reason why fat persons are often considered "jolly" is because of this bubbling volubility of their high moods often stimulated by company.) So remember, during the inevitable down phases, he who feels deflated must once have been a balloon, and affirm your intent not to let this balloon psychology be manifested in your physical shape. Affirm your intent to float on the crest of the next wave and avoid pain by taking pains in preparing for renewed endeavor. Keep a weight chart; but don't be discouraged by fluctuations because it is more important that the graph should show you have made repeated efforts to triumph. Even when you break your resolution, you can at least resolve to go on making new resolutions. It might help to keep a mood chart parallel to that for pounds and compare the two graphs.

A rancher had a wild horse which he wished to bring to pasture. Since no one could do anything with the spirited creature, he tied it to a mule he had owned for years. For a long while the horse consistently resisted the mule's desire to return home by making long excursions into the countryside, but the mule never ceased tugging and dragging in the direction of the barn until finally, without even realizing it, the horse was brought in. In this way, the mind can finally have its way with the body and the power of fixed intent overcomes undisciplined spurts of perverse desire.

Even after you have achieved your ideal weight it is necessary to allow for natural fluctuations. Just try to keep them in bounds, and that boundary's topmost margin still within range of your proper poundage. Let there be one particular mark at which you take a stand saying, "Here I shall remain and beyond this point I absolutely will not go!" Then endeavor to keep your daily level at least five pounds below this danger zone.

To continue as a successful dieter you will have to realize that this is no temporary discipline, but an enduring way of life. For this reason you might as well stabilize your weight where it belongs, instead of pounds over normal, since it takes the same discipline to hold the line high as low. Alcoholics never lose their affinity for liquor and you will feel the same way about food. Only instead of cushioning yourself against the blows of fate with fat, your cushion will be the capacity to give in and bounce back mentally, without losing your basic equilibrium.

4. Substitute gratitude for criticism.

During most of our formal education emphasis is laid upon the sharpening of our critical faculties. We are made to feel naive or foolish for being enthusiastic about things not approved by the recognized taste-masters of the day. To be called simple is an insult. Frequently young people affect a jaded attitude in the hope of appearing more worldly and sophisticated and then, inexorably, the depreciatory mask is stamped on the face which wore it.

Thinking back over the instruction you received, ask yourself how much training was ever given in gratitude, real tolerance and appreciation of the contributions of others, particularly those not recognized as standard authorities. The universal penchant of our age to criticize, has become a cultural warp so ingrained, we are hardly aware of its destructive effects. Instead we make a sport of spotting and analyzing weaknesses in people. Our political system has become predicated on the ability of leaders to demonstrate superiority by showing where others have failed. Statesmen set upon one another like fighting cocks out for blood, as the public rests back to enjoy the show.

The word "grateful" is an amalgam of "great" and "full." The person who feels gratitude endows and enhances with his appreciation. He puts more into a situation than he asks of it and, in giving of himself, is open to receive and identify with something larger than the self. He has no *need* to be stuffing himself with food or flattery because he is already filled with a sense of wonder and sufficiency in finding the world so full of greatness. Nor does he brood over wrongs done to him, because to be grateful means also to understand and forgive and begin again. It is said that to understand is to forgive. To understand perfectly is to know there is nothing to forgive.

The food addict must, therefore, do something more than merely analyze his problems. To analyze is not to understand; it is only the midway point. Critical analysis is like dissecting a blossom to discover the secret of its blooming, whereas sympathetic understanding feeds the roots which literally "stand under" the plant. It is the incentive for growth itself, the light and warmth which encourages flowering.

To counteract the oral characteristic of feeling forever deprived, and substitute the healing strength of gratitude, it may be necessary to prime the pump in small ways such as saying grace before meals (it need be but a few seconds of silence), and offering a mental thank you for pleasures and favors often taken for granted. So many people pray for divine blessings, yet have not the human graciousness to say a word of thanks for those received.

The greatest saints and sages the world has known have always been characterized by their complete acceptance of others. Anyone, no matter how reprehensible a sinner, can come to such a master and be taken into the fold, to be cared for and redeemed. To the enlightened soul there can be nothing so low, so unlovely or unloved that compassion can not make it significant. Each life is a tapestry. The knots and loose ends may show on the outside, but it is woven into a design of rare beauty on the inner side. The variety of such patterns only adds richness to the fabric. In invoking your master-self try to see from within. Receive yourself graciously, that you may return your tolerance, kindness and encouragement to the world.

Control in eating, or in living, comes not by splitting the psyche into fragments through critical analysis, but by accepting and cooperating with the wisdom of the guiding self within. It is not a question of one part giving orders and the other obeying or protesting, but rather of these parts being rightfully integrated. In the last analysis there can be only synthesis.

5. Thin-k.

To "think thin" is, first, to think. The thin is already contained within the larger word. This means to substitute for physical expansion the mental enlargement of hobbies, interests and creative entertainment. Staying active and on the go, mentally or physically, not only brushes the cobwebs from your psyche and keeps it a shining mirror to reflect the world, but distracts your attention from kitchens, restaurants and obvious places of temptation. Educated people are more likely to be slender, not just because their minds keep them exercised, but because their diverse interests afford roots and psychological substance to assimilate.

It is a fact that obesity is commonly found in immigrants of the first or second generation. Not only are these people bound by barriers of custom and language, but often they have lost their cultural roots and compensate by drawing upon the nourishment of food. Mealtime becomes the known and familiar ground of their lives. Not only do their weight problems stubbornly resist all efforts at amelioration, but they often are not even recognized as existing.

With maturity and the decreasing caloric requirements of the body, it becomes increasingly important to cultivate habits of going to museums, lectures, concerts, church or library, rather than to teas, cocktail and dinner parties. Such intellectual interests prevent you from becoming a psychological immigrant, alien to your innate spiritual needs and responses. Young people tend to do active things for entertainment such as dancing, swimming, skiing or tennis, but with aging, eating becomes a primary diversion.

There are many reasons for this shift of emphasis. Older people generally have more money and can afford to eat out more. They have time to linger over food and make it the focal point of the day. Their taste buds, along with other senses, may have become less acute and so they search for highly flavored or unusual tasting repasts. Having less strength they seek more passive amusements. Think, for example, what you would do to entertain a couple who are about seventy. Chances are you would either have them come to your home for dinner or take them out to a restaurant for heavy food and light conversation.

Many find themselves in the position of the former football star who sighed: "I used to be quite an athlete — big chest, hard stomach. But now all that is behind me."

Thinking does not mean abstract speculation but involves coming up with a plan for action. This takes us on to the next point — how to upgrade our mental activity.

6. Sublimate.

Once you have galvanized yourself into a show of positive behavior, the necessity arises to make it a meaningful part of your over-all pattern of living. Along with major innovations in hobbies or career, note small tokens of progress such as when you purchase a good magazine instead of a candy bar or write a card to a sick friend instead of taking a coffee and doughnut break. Try buying a child an ice cream cone, instead of one for yourself, and listen to what he has to say. Donations to charity help, but when possible donate the actual time normally given to food consumption.

Acquiring and feeding a young pet pays substantial dividends in honest affection and in developing your sensitivity to unspoken need. Love can be shared with a cherished dog or cat, permitting a spontaneity not always possible in human relationships. Gardening also establishes rapport with nature and makes a productive avocation for old and young, even if it is only to keep plants in a window, construct dish gardens or arrange dried flowers. It is noteworthy how few avid gardeners, bird-watchers, shell-gatherers or other naturalists get fat. This observation supports statistics which show that city dwellers are decidedly more prone to obesity than people living in the country.

Unfortunately people who tend to be timid, anxious and weight-prone are more likely to be incapacitated by the immobilization of their aggressive impulses. Many are afraid to swim, dislike walking, and rebel against any kind of active exercise. They are especially suspicious of nature in the raw, which appears to them disorderly and uncontrolled. Dirt is just plain dirty rather than a substance to make things grow, and they fear it irrationally. Yet all the time they court the real killers of sloth and fat.

The vast TOPS organization, abbreviating their purpose in the slogan "Take Off Pounds Sensibly," gives primary emphasis to the safety factor. Yet they play down the importance of exercise. Never was it more true that fear itself is most to be feared — fat being fear's furthest outpost. The difficulty in facing up to the real enemy is expressed in a bulky comedian's lugubrious lament, "No matter how fast I turn, my backside is still behind me." The recalcitrance of such fears is shown by the fact that some oral types manage to remain remarkably slender, but produce fat children in compensation.

The apathy and listlessness observed in the seriously overweight comes not just from the burden of flesh they bear, but from this fundamental disconnection from nature, within and without. "I don't know what I want," they say, or "It's no use running around in circles just for distraction." Those who have done some amateur psychologising will assert, "There is no sense wasting my time taking up hobbies and charity work when I know the trouble is really in me. First I should find out what is wrong with myself."

The fallacy is that you can not find yourself through introspection alone. If self-analysis were the answer then psychiatrists would have better luck treating obese persons. As it is, they admit there is practically nothing they can do. Enthusiasm and outgoing concern, like other talents, must be earned and constantly cultivated. It may take some extra effort or therapeutic assistance to unclog the channel but, as blockages dissolve, interests automatically increase without undue forcing.

Fat, like money, is crystallized energy. If hoarded it produces an imbalance in your body's economy. Enthusiasm is a liberating force that releases these resources back into circulation and effects spiritual gain through a wealth of enriching experiences.

Sublimation must, therefore, be a transformation and not just a substitution of some randomly selected social activity for one with less prestige. It is the release of mental force and the quality of caring that makes sublimation meaningful, not the apparent results. If at first the process must be forced, as you would scrape together the financing for a daring venture, try to remember the two men who were cast into the sea after a shipwreck.

"Help!" the first one cried, feeling himself sinking. "I can't swim!"

His companion, striking out against the waves, shouted back, "Fake it!"

Real effort, even to "fake it," will produce correspondingly real results.

7. Let the magic work from within.

It is a wise woman who inaugurates a diet by cutting down on makeup and tight foundation garments. Avoidance of artificial props can help melt the chrysalis which prevents your caterpillar-nature from emerging as a butterfly. Let your concern for others go out on radiant-hued wings and observe how much nicer people become. Concentrate on improving their image in your eyes, rather than just your own. The beautiful butterfly of love for others may, upon close examination, still resemble the original worm of self-love, but who would notice as it flies freely in the sunshine. Only remember, if you would be a butterfly, you will have to make the blubber fly.

Ask yourself to what extent your clothes and cosmetics are designed to reveal *you* and to what extent they are designed to conceal. How much of your beauty comes from loving kindness and how much from your pocketbook? In what proportion do you feel these factors determine the attractiveness of others? What is your ideal of beauty?

A man can undertake a similar self-examination by asking himself if he keeps his own body in as good shape as he keeps his car. Which is deemed worthy of the larger investment in time, money and concern? Just as some women become abjectly dependent on their cosmetically created faces and hairdos, many men identify with the form of their car, investing it with all the attributes of power, drive and efficiency they wish to make their own. A fascinating comparison can be made of human types and the cars they drive. For example, not many fat men drive sports cars. In primitive times, tribes had totems such as the bear, wolf or leopard to suggest the ideal of superhuman potency. Now our totems are likely to be cars.

Some of us identify with the roles we play more than with symbolic vehicles of form and locomotion. Mothers are supposed to look "motherly," bankers "solid," merchants "prosperous" and politicians "affable." We settle into the routine of parent, church-goer, employee or boss, until finally we scarcely realize that we are still actors, who must someday doff all disguises and account to ourselves alone. What then will be left, when all the parts have been played and we step away from the footlights to confront ourselves in our essential being as, in truth, we have always been? Could it be possible to recollect ourselves throughout the performance and so be playwrights as well as actors? Why not pull the strings instead of being just a puppet? The real drama could be the story of your determination to be the hero or heroine, the beautiful and the beloved, rather than the type in which you may have found yourself so rudely miscast.

8. Exercise.

Although we have a section on hows and whys of exercise, we stress its importance here because it helps make you realize what you are inside your clothes, car and social facade, and what you can become. A young boy who had just completed a course in judo and weight lifting replied to a companion's belligerent behavior with the warning, "Don't fool around with me any more, because I have muscles now, where before I didn't even have *places*!" The places were psychologically invisible until he was able to realize their potential.

We wish to put special emphasis on the importance of leg exercises in a lying position. The fundamental motions given in the next section can be varied with crosswise, circular and swinging stretches. These serve to counteract the lack of backbone feeling so frequently experienced by oral types. Strengthening your legs and the lower half of your body is directly related to encouraging the capacity for independence and standing on your feet. Solid contact must be made with the earth before reaching for the stars. Just because your feet are on the ground does not mean that your eyes must also rest there. But you can stand erect, look up and assert your independence only to the extent that you also realize your dependence upon the ground which supports and sustains all life. He who would master nature must first serve her.

At first glance, literal interpretations of the meaning of physical positions may seem far-fetched, as when we point out that strengthening the legs promotes better "understanding" of yourself or that stretching out on the ground helps you get "back to nature." But experience has shown that the division between body and mind is nebulous. Getting into a new position really can change your outlook on things; stretching your limbs gives the idea of reaching beyond old levels of achievement, and learning to bend your back can make you more flexible mentally. It is a long established principle of psychosomatic medicine that people who have burdens too heavy to shoulder are prone to bursitis. Those who "can't stomach" a situation often develop ulcers, and psychologically stiff-necked types really do seem to thicken in the neck or retract their heads like a turtle. The fact that the mind affects the body is beyond question, but research has hardly begun into the equally fascinating area of how deliberately induced changes in the body can affect the mental outlook on life, and so permit the mind to work on itself *through* the body.

Many oral people are deeply afraid of losing control. For this reason they are sometimes fearful of airplane travel, swimming and other situations epitomizing their feelings of rootlessness and alienation from the earth below. Anything which increases their power of self-control, as does exercise, is particularly reassuring.

Exercise also enhances sexual allure and potency. In many people the cerebral functions seem cut off from instinct, and their desires are short-circuited. Flexibility, strength and proper alignment of your back keeps the channel open and circulates energy throughout your system.

As we point out in our later discussion of sex versus food types of people, there is nothing like a satisfying romance to distract attention from eating. A psychoanalyst would say that the genital stage comes later than the oral, both in terms of infant development and psychological maturity. With the awakening of the sexual instincts the libido is directed toward the "real" world of interpersonal relationships. The world within may be just as inherently real, but can have no meaning until connected with external circumstances.

Many homosexuals are "mama's boys," still fixated at the oral stage and hence prone to alcoholism and infantile jealousy due to a basic sense of insecurity. Sometimes physical exercise and athletics can precipitate a borderline case into manhood, simply by promoting harmonious development of all faculties in an orderly pattern, leading naturally into sexual maturity.

When a person is overweight the body creates useless cells. Many of these cells are faulty because of improper messages transmitted to the reproduction mechanism, just as a piece of carbon paper used too many times starts making blurred copies. When a population declines due to famine, the sick, old and weak are eliminated. The same thing happens to the useless cells within your body. Although you may feel uncomfortable while the internal famine rages, the combination of diet and exercise will throw off weak and useless cells until the image your body reproduces becomes concise and clear again.

One exercise which can be recommended for even the most awkward or overweight person is called Elbow Bending. If you can master this difficult position you need never again be prey to pounds. To accomplish it you first seat yourself in a chair at a table. Place one hand on the table in a relaxed manner. Close your mouth and breathe only through your nose. Now very slowly raise your hand to your mouth and touch it. Then, without opening your mouth, lower your hand back to the table. When you can do this exercise successfully at the meal table, you possess a most potent weapon in the war on fat.

9. Objectify

So now you have followed all the rules and are still hungry. No need to fly into a panic, much less for the pantry shelves. The stomach may grumble but you need not identify with it. Let it complain. While it is sending out its disagreeable lament, you send up a prayer for the millions on this planet who never receive adequate nourishment and yet endure. There are much worse discomforts than a few pangs which will pass. Fat, for example, can be a whole lot worse. Probably, in the past, you have cheerfully managed to overlook pains of other kinds far more acute than those you now fear.

Meanwhile the distracting sensation indicates success, because

already your body, like a parsimonious miser, is being reluctant-
ly forced to draw upon available resources. Be glad the excess
fat is going. Don't moan, "*I* am hungry," but think instead,
"A sensation of hunger is doing its best to overpower me."
This will help to keep it at a safe distance.

If you start to grab for food, do not stand before the refrigerator like a zombie, but focus attention consciously on what you
are doing. Be fully aware of your actions and of the cross-
currents of desire contending in your mind. Observe what is
taking place, as though from a detached position. With hand
midway to your mouth, stop and ask yourself, is this trip necessary? Return the food to the plate and imagine you have eaten
it. Then, if you must, give in and gobble, but only because
you have decided it is the best course in the present situation.

The moment you become conscious of something you have a
chance of controlling it. Often, mere awareness of the impulse
to stuff will dissipate its energy. Then, as you survey the field
of conflict objectively, you can deliberately muster your force
of will, like a well-informed commander-in-chief.

Objectification can involve many levels of self-confrontation.
The following example is an experiment all seam-spreaders
and zipper-rippers are urged to try. First weigh yourself. Then
check a weight table to see how much you should weigh. Sub-
tract this amount from your actual poundage, to show the
amount of excess baggage you are habitually carrying. Let us
suppose it is twenty-five pounds. Find some object weighing
that much and tie it about your waist. Carry it around for a
while. The relief you will feel in setting it down will treat
you to a preview of how you will feel after ridding yourself of
your extra girth.

Many fat people think they are completely normal and quite
attractive because they have contrived never to see themselves
as they are seen. We suggest that when you look at yourself
in a mirror you don't just focus on your face. Arrange to have
a full-length looking glass and study your whole profile,
stomach, waist and hips, with no clothes on. This can be a
most en-lightening experience.

One woman took an unflattering side-view snapshot of herself in a bathing suit, had it enlarged to enormous proportions, and taped it inside her refrigerator door. Another placed an exercise mat directly in front of the kitchen food shelves, reminding her to have a workout to justify the reward of food.

The pinch test indicates where you stand among members of the Great Society. Using thumb and index finger, pinch yourself directly above the navel, at the side below the first rib, and underneath the upper arm. If you grasp an inch or more of fat between your fingers, hold on and just contemplate it for a while in silence. Anything more than an inch should not be there.

Self-confrontation, we warn you, is only for the strong, or for those who wish to be strong. It is like the situation of a king who has never bothered much about ruling his country. Suddenly he decides that he is going to hold court, establish democratic procedures and listen to the grievances of his subjects. If he really intends to hear, heed, and take constructive measures this is fine and he will have a better country. But if he just listens to complaints and does nothing to remedy the wrongs which come to his attention, then he is in a much worse position than before because his subjects are now aware of their troubles, and having made formal complaints will demand some sort of justice. Having been stirred from their apathy by the hope of improved treatment, they may even rebel when their plight is not alleviated. If, therefore, you are going to objectify, realize that it is contingent on you to take some positive action toward rectifying the problems which arise.

10. Visualize your ideal.

Having taken a look at the shadows within, turn your face again to the world of light. Construct a vivid mental picture of the way you would like to be, endowing your thought image with all the mental and moral attributes you admire. The form should be realistic, in that it represents the essence of the finer qualities inherent in your nature and which you, to some extent, are capable of actualizing. Consider that the object of your striving is not so much an external change, as a *release* of the true being within, even as a sculptor might be said to liberate his vision from the encasing material.

A five to fifteen minute morning meditation each day serves to refocus your intent and beam it toward clarifying the hours ahead. Those too preoccupied to find the time for formal meditation can endeavor to cultivate an introspective attitude of deliberate reflection upon the meaning and purpose of passing events.

Meditation is not a passive reverie. It is a discipline requiring trained capacity to concentrate and visualize. Nor is it quite the same as prayer. Prayer beseeches and entreats, but meditation is an endeavor to tune in on and receive available guidance. Prayer petitions, "Hear Lord, for Thy servant speaketh." Meditation requests, "Speak Lord, for Thy servant listeneth." Prayer is usually addressed to an external, transcendent deity, while meditation is a stilling of the mind for the purpose of discovering that god-like powers can be found in the human heart and soul. Prayer constructs a channel to higher realms, but the vacuum created by meditation permits forces to flow through from the reservoir of the larger Life. A "miserable sinner" can pray, but in order to meditate you must believe in yourself.

Whether you call your daily communion prayer or meditation, the important thing is that this practice should prove effective in bringing your life of action and thought into harmony with the deeper source of your being. The religiously oriented person can say that this also involves cooperation with God's plan and purpose. Still we should not depreciate the necessity for taking the initiative. Somehow He always does His part when we do ours, as in the instance of the parson who leaned over his neighbor's fence and benevolently remarked, "That is a fine garden you and God have made."

"Yup," the neighbor remarked good-humoredly. "And you should of seen it when God had it alone."

Cultivating your own garden is a kind of meditation demonstrably more effective than asking some distant or external power for aid. Begging help without taking action betrays the same dependency as a reliance on excessive food, drink, or superficial techniques which would reform the world without changing the performers in it. We are better advised to reformulate our own thoughts, motives and desires and be thankful that life has given us this capacity.

In Conclusion: Let us remember that our attitude toward food is an inevitable outcome of our attitude toward life. Food or events not assimilated by the organism no longer serve to create an integrated body of expression, but poison the system with toxic by-products. The result is increased craving for satiation with diminished satisfaction of real needs.

It is not necessarily the particular food or circumstances that cause trouble. The healthy organism can eliminate what is not required in the same way that it can ward off disease. The trouble comes from an inability to subsume the materials ingested to the modus operandi of the body or personality. Even negative happenings can be incorporated into some greater good, just as the body needs to contend with disease germs to manufacture the antibodies that strengthen its defenses. Our positive benefit lies in transforming that which is given into meaningful accomplishment, that we in turn may be transformed for the sake of a larger Purpose.

All our attitudes — whether toward eating, loving or existing — reflect this capacity to relate what is experienced to the self that does the experiencing. Only then can we possess all that is ours, and be by ourselves possessed.

The Lazy Man's Exer-size Plan

PART TWO

The Lazy Man's Exer-size Plan

1

Hows and Whys of Exercise

FEELING UNCOMFORTABLE ABOUT YOUR WEIGHT arouses deep-seated anxieties. You must work hard catering to these fears and forego, for their sake, many of life's choicest pleasures. If you want to succeed in self-reconstruction you must make up your mind that you are going to be too lazy to continue struggling under this combined burden of weight and worry. Somehow you must let it all go.

The first fear to jettison is the fear of exercise. The over-weight are notoriously reluctant to exert, lest they hurt themselves. You might think this sense of danger is a result of being excessively large and perhaps clumsy, but that is not entirely true. The anxiety that contributed to producing the fat in the first place mitigates against experimenting with new forms of movement.

There is no excuse for not exercising and the sooner this is admitted, the sooner you are free to face real and fundamental problems. Books, television, local classes and country clubs point the way, and certainly anyone smart enough to read has the intelligence to think up new and interesting methods of keeping fit. Fortunately the best exercises are also the simplest. Leg-raising, push-ups and toe-touching can be done without concern for equipment, money, time, place or outfit.

If you are one of the unpleasingly plump who are not exercising regularly you may wish to analyze why you have not taken measures to stay in shape. This can be the first step on your road to success. Prepare for resistance from the body which, like an untrained pet, will try to evade the lesson and suggest other games. Study these resistances. This can be the real game if you are willing to meet the challenge.

Exercise is essential for the following physical reasons.

1. It burns calories, converting matter into the energy of life.
2. It stimulates essential glandular secretions.
3. It coordinates your nervous system, developing your kinesthetic sense.
4. It improves posture by keeping your back supple and strong.
5. It combats stiffness in joints and ligaments.
6. It increases circulation so that veins and arteries stay elastic.
7. It promotes deep breathing and oxygenation of your entire system.
8. It tones muscles which hold your vital organs in place.
9. It builds up endurance.
10. It makes you a desirable and exciting sexual partner.

Exercise produces the following psychological benefits.

1. It sublimates stress, making tensions work constructively rather than destructively.
2. It salves the conscience and hence combats anxiety and fear.
3. It leads to self-confrontation, forcing you to take account of assets and liabilities.
4. It heals the rift between body and mind, promoting integration of the personality.
5. It bolsters confidence when improvement is noted.
6. It leads to interesting contacts with vital, active people.

All of these benefits, physical and psychological, form the basis for a beautiful figure, sexual allure, health and vigor.

Everyone admits that exercise is a good idea — for other people. One reason why many never undertake a personally rewarding program is because they think it will be hard work. They fail to realize that the law of reverse effort applies here as elsewhere. There are ways of stretching and bending simply by allowing the body to let go. These are not only as effective as violent calisthenics, but induce a gentler more relaxed way of life which, in turn, allows more time for appreciation of living. We are encouraging you to try a system which works best when the action is relaxed, the movements controlled, and the routine one of restraint and repose. It is all right to be lazy, providing you know what you are doing.

Probably the first lazy thing you will have to do is to think of some activity you don't particularly enjoy, and then eliminate it in order to make time for your new program. It is surprising how many nonessentials clutter up our days. Trimming down on these is a first-rate exercise in itself, and proves that you have the will to exorcise the spirit of unnecessary accumulation, known as the "stuffing syndrome."

The rules for maintaining your routine are few and simple.

1. RESTRAINT.

Always move slowly while exercising. No matter how jittery your nerves may be, do not allow your motions to betray even the least sense of rush or hurry. Watching a group of fat people giggling, guffawing and jerking themselves through an exercise session is just about the most dismaying sight imaginable. Don't even move your tongue more than necessary but concentrate silently on what you are doing.

A sign of your progress will be your ability to move more slowly and to maintain a position longer, with fewer violent efforts. It never helps to bounce about, frenetically attempting this or that exercise. Work purposefully through a specific series and then go on to more if you are able, but always in slow motion.

The restraint cultivated through holding each posture will translate into restraint in the kitchen and at the dinner table.

2. SELF-AWARENESS.

Always know what you are doing and why you are doing it. If to slowness of motion, you add the endeavor to be completely aware of everything the body does, you have ideal insurance against damaging yourself. Be conscious not only of your physical movements, but of the mental attitudes that accompany them and of the feelings they engender. It is useless to try to touch your toes if you are hating yourself for not being able to do it. The psyche will rebel and make some excuse for avoiding the effort.

For some people exercise opens veritable floodgates of self-depreciation. It can, therefore, serve as a kind of psychoanalysis if you are able to achieve constructive release. You may be surprised at the potency of the negative thoughts that come to the surface when you discover all the things you can't do, but at least you are in a position to cope with these recognized feelings of insufficiency and to give them a fair fight. Now you begin to understand why the body originally got into trouble.

Exercise also serves as a do-it-yourself analysis, because it takes you back to the child stage, when you were first discovering the body and what it could accomplish. Many people feel pathetically vulnerable in their trunks or leotards, as though their defenses were down. Indeed, many potential students will not attend exercise classes because it goes against the grain psychologically to have to take off their shoes, get down on the floor, and be like a little child again. As children many of us were taught to mistrust our instincts and repress all spontaneity. Now is the time to relearn and approach each new experience with fresh appreciation, as you advance through retreat.

You can tell if you are succeeding in reeducating your senses, by whether or not you become bored with the routine. The more you apply yourself, the more fresh and gratifying each position will seem. There will always be new discoveries to make about yourself and your reactions. If you feel dulled or jaded by repetition, then you have missed the point. Exercise should be no more boring than eating. Aim for immediacy of awareness, direct knowledge of your body and responsiveness to its needs. You can pick up the telephone and call any city you please. Can you communicate as easily with your big toe?

3. RELAXATION.

First and foremost try to relax, even when engaged in utmost exertion. You may be surprised to find that these two modes are not mutually exclusive. Muscles which would have signaled pain if they were rigid will let go and allow you to stretch or bend without discomfort, if only you can persuade them to cooperate. Once you have mastered the art of relaxing, even while your body is in a position of deliberately induced stress, you will find it easier to relax when the children shriek, or the budget fails to balance or the house hasn't been picked up.

Not only should you master the art of relaxing your whole body under tension, thus avoiding the dangers of straining, but you should learn the techniques of relaxing one part while another is fully stretched. When a hypnotist lectured for a group of yoga students and their friends and he said "Tense your right fist," all the nonstudents grimaced while those previously trained in exercise retained tranquil expressions. Sometimes it helps just to keep the appearance of repose even when aggravated. It is harder to be angry if you deliberately unclench the fists and allow your fingers to dangle freely.

The purpose of restraint and controlled relaxation is to confine necessary tensions to the places where they can do some good and not allow points of leakage through which the energy of your body dribbles wastefully away. Keep your steam in to run your own engine and do not permit it to escape and befog your mind or cloud the lives of others.

Be sure to lie down flat on the floor after *each* exercise and relax for a few moments. Practice deep relaxation (Floating) at the end, with deep breathing and autosuggestion, preferably for five minutes. We suggest that you begin your exercise program *after* you have studied the section dealing with techniques of breathing and autosuggestion.

4. REGULARITY.

In the beginning be a slave to routine. Go through the same exercises, in the same order, as automatically as you would comb your hair or brush your teeth. They are every bit as important as other daily necessities you wouldn't dream of neglecting, including eating. Choose one or two to start, and then when you have mastered them go on to others, still keeping the original order. There is much benefit in learning to do something better even though you thought you were already doing it perfectly.

Fifteen minutes a day of exercising is enough for most people, and more advantageous than a couple of hours once a week. It is better not to set unrealistic goals for the future, but to start with a program that allows room for improvement. Once you have demonstrated an ability to persist, go on until your solid foundations connect with your castles in the air. A great advantage of making exercise habitual is that soon you become so used to it that you cease to look for results, and are agreeably surprised when improvements begin to show.

It isn't necessary to exercise a great deal, if it is done with regularity, because all the rest of the time you are standing, moving and breathing more effectively and so the improvement becomes self-sustaining. What counts is that you feed certain information about how the body should conduct itself into the computer of the subconscious mind. Once your daily data card is filled in and properly presented, your psychic machinery will continue to sort and digest the orders and come up with the proper action to carry them out.

Many of the exercises we have given need to be performed only once, if you can put enough will and intensity into the effort you are making. You can be like a general giving a command and then sitting back to allow vast armies of cells within to march about your body carrying out the designated strategy. A good general should not have to repeat his orders too many times but he should always be in command and, as much as possible, on the scene that he may inspire his troops with the knowledge of his presence. The time you spend relaxing after each exercise is not wasted. Exercise, like food, must be assimilated and digested. Doing too many things too fast sets up a state of internal confusion that can be fatiguing out of proportion to the energy actually expended.

5. NONCOMPETITIVENESS.

While motivation is essential, nothing wrecks a performance as devastatingly as the tension which comes from caring too much. Tests given to university students showed that forcing them to compete for high rewards invariably diminished the overall efficiency of their problem solving. Rats in a maze would quickly find their goal if they were starved for a short time. When deprived too long they became frantic and required three times as many trials to find the food offered for their reward. In these experiments social scientists have affirmed the law of reverse effort. We all know that one can be too hungry to eat, too tired to sleep, or have worked too hard for something to care when it comes at last. On the positive side, all good things do come to the one who can afford to wait and do the job right.

Many people grow up thinking they hate exercise, when what they really resent is the competitive spirit engendered in many sports and games. Often they know they are not up to their best under such circumstances. Frequently it is the more intelligent students in school who refuse to be taken in by the futile competition of athletic programs, and so the idea of having a good mind becomes dissociated from the ideal of physical well-being.

Overweight adolescents frequently eat no more than others, but they exercise less. That is enough to make all the difference and set a lifetime pattern of shunning activity and avoiding the challenge of striving to surpass previous capabilities. Most fat people are speaking the truth when they say they don't eat much. They forget that they are burning less. A group of obese university students were provided with a reducing diet of 1200 calories a day. Part of the group also undertook a program of brisk walking for two hours a day. Those who did not do the walking lost an average of three pounds a week, while those who did averaged a loss of five pounds, felt more fit, and suffered no more from hunger than nonexercisers. Over a year, the difference between exercise and nonexercise on such a diet would add up to one hundred and four pounds!

Since much of the anxiety and defensiveness which leads to overweight grows out of the fear of failure engendered by too much competition, the answer lies in having a system at which you can't fail, because failure isn't built into the game. The ideal should be to make ends and means the same, so that the pleasure lies, as much as possible, in the doing and not just in the outcome. One does not listen to a symphony being played in breathless anticipation of what the ending will be, but rather to delight in the music of each moment. It is not the future ahead with which we are concerned, as much as the future in the sense of an inner potential to be liberated.

Cultivate a sensuous awareness in every gesture and expression, but avoid any self-consciousness that may come from the idea that there is something peculiar or unnatural in this introspective discipline. Steam and electricity have always existed in the atmosphere, but only recently has man harnessed them for his use. You also can maintain a pragmatic attitude toward releasing the mighty energies within you, as you experiment with the technology of self-knowledge.

6. ENJOY.

If you are not feeling rested, stimulated and encouraged after your exercise session, then something is wrong. Either you are performing the wrong exercises, or else doing the right ones incorrectly. If you will read back over the rules and tips you can probably find out what is amiss. Maybe you have been too intense, trying to *make* things go, instead of *letting* go.

Your health should also pick up. Expect improvement, remembering that cheerful people resist ailments better than glum ones. "The surly bird catches the germ." Aspire to be light and free, radiantly vital and alive. Exercise of the will-to-enjoy is the final magic ingredient which transforms work into play, and makes the play for real.

2

Your Basic Routine

FOLLOW EACH EXERCISE with a period of silent relaxation and deep breathing in the supine position. You should practice without shoes, on a carpet, firm mat or folded blanket.

1. THE ROCK AND ROLL

a. Lie on your back, bend and raise your knees, clasping them to your chest with both hands interlocked behind knees. Raise your head toward your knees and slowly rock back and forth on your curved spine. Gradually increase the length of your movements to and fro. With proficiency you will be able to sit with your knees clasped to your chest, feet flat on the floor, and rock back until your toes touch the floor behind your head.

b. More advanced students can practice this exercise starting from the sitting position, with legs crossed and knees bent. Clasp right toes with left hand and left toes with right hand. Bend your head forward until it comes as close to the floor as possible. Then rock back on rounded spine as before, still clasping toes, until your feet come up over your head and, if possible, toes touch the floor behind. Repeat until the motion begins to seem easier and you feel a sense of rhythm.

This do-it-yourself rock will warm you up for greater things, but do not underestimate its importance in making you use your whole body in one coordinated effort. It massages and stimulates the whole vertebral column. Concentrate on the roundness of your back and smoothness of motion.

2. THE PUMP

Lie flat on your back and raise your right leg slowly while breathing in. Lower your leg and breathe out. Repeat with your left leg. Continue five to ten times, alternating sides, and synchronize your breathing with leg movements. Then repeat, using both legs at once.

The secret of this exercise is to stretch your legs to the utmost without bending your knees. Your toes should be pointed. Imagine as you raise your leg that it is in traction and being pulled from the toes by a spring or elastic. Make a concentrated effort to relax the rest of your body and retain a serene expression. This enables you to control tension in one part of your body, without allowing it to spread to other parts where it can exert no constructive effects. Consequently it conserves energy. This exercise strengthens your back and stomach muscles and improves your posture.

3. THE HINGE

Lying on your back raise your legs with straight knees to an angle of forty-five degrees (midway up from floor) and hold. Your heels should remain suspended about two feet above the floor. The effect of maintaining the position without motion is to direct the vital forces inward to the work of strengthening muscles, rather than outward in unnecessary movement. Maintain this position as long as possible without undue discomfort.

4. THE RUSTY HINGE

Lie flat and raise your legs with straight knees, until your thighs are just barely off the floor and hold. Your heels should be only a *few* inches off the ground. Hold this position until you start to feel uncomfortable. This is an exercise which is extremely effective in toning up your abdominal muscles.

5. THE SWIVEL SLIMMER

Lying as before, extend straight arms, palms on floor, at a forty-five degree angle from your body. Inhale and raise your legs, keeping your heels a *few* inches off the floor with your knees together and straight throughout. Swing your legs as far as you can to the right. Ideally they should make a ninety degree angle with your torso. You can rotate your legs when swinging to the side, until your left leg is on top of your right one. Then raise both legs up toward your stomach until they are in line with your body. Then slowly lower them back down on the right until your heels are two inches from the floor. Then swing your legs with heels close to the floor, back to the center position. Repeat on the left side. Two or three of these rotations will prove most efficacious in toning up the muscles which hold you in at the waist.

6. THE CAT

a. Get down on your hands and knees, keeping your back parallel to the floor and your arms and legs perpendicular to the floor. Point your fingers inward with tips barely touching. You should look like a table whose legs extend straight down. Inhale and by bending your elbows lower your chest until it comes close to or, preferably, touches the floor. Your fingers should remain touching and motionless. The base of your neck should rest on your fingers, with your chin extended forward. Your midback should curve in like a cat's. Hold ten to thirty seconds and then return to the table position by reversing the above procedure.

b. Kneeling as before, inhale, raise your head as high as possible and extend your right leg high behind you, with your knee straight. Hold several seconds until a pull is felt along your whole back. Exhale while returning to the starting position. Then repeat, using your left leg.

c. Still kneeling, raise your right knee in under your body towards your chest, press your chin to your chest and try to touch your knee to your forehead. Your spine should stretch the opposite way from before (b). Even though you may have difficulty connecting your knee and forehead, keep on pressing in. Repeat with your other leg.

The cat-like stretches tone up your entire body and are safe for bad backs, since your spine does not counter the pull of gravity and is not compressed. It is also useful as a test for posture. People with round or hunched shoulders will experience difficulty in lowering the chest to the floor and will feel a strong backward pull in their shoulder region. If the Cat is difficult for you, take it as a signal to work on your upper back and shoulders.

For beginners and non-athletic types, these positions make a complete routine. The Rock and Roll works on your whole spine, the Pump mainly on your stomach, legs and lower back, and the Cat on your upper back, arms and neck. These are preliminary to the Shoulderstand and other, more advanced positions. Just as a baby wants to walk after he has learned to crawl, so will you want to progress and improve your performance after you have mastered this series.

7. THE INVERTED POSTURE

Lying flat on your back, inhale deeply and raise both legs together slowly, with your knees straight and heels together, until your hips are off the ground. Press your palms and forearms down to give leverage and lift. Then support your lower back with your hands, placing your palms on buttocks and sliding your hands along hips until your thumb is on top of your pelvic bone and your fingers extend around your waist to the small of your back. Use your elbows to prop up your buttocks. Tilt your legs back over your head so that your whole body curves. Hold this position for a minute or as long as is comfortable, trying to remain motionless. Then reverse this procedure and *slowly* return to the starting position.

It may be necessary at the start to jerk your legs and bend your knees in order to raise your hips from the ground but this is a compromise measure. Ideally the exercise should be accomplished in one long smooth motion. Try to keep your legs straight the whole time, letting your spine do the curving.

8. THE SHOULDERSTAND

This is a continuation of the Inverted Posture to the point where your whole body is vertical, with your hands giving support to your back. Your chin is deliberately pressed into the top of your chest. Hold for as much as three minutes, but avoid overdoing at first. Athletic people can slowly raise their arms along their thighs, until balancing on neck and shoulders. Your legs may be swung slightly in toward your face to maintain balance. The Shoulderstand should not be attempted if you are uncomfortable in the Inverted Posture, or if you find it necessary to jerk your body up into position. Return to a lying position as slowly as possible, feeling each part of your back successively curving down to the floor.

Benefits derived from the Shoulderstand and the Inverted Posture are described in the next chapter.

9. THE PLOW

To accomplish the Plow take the Shoulderstand position and bring both feet down over your head, keeping your knees straight. Eventually your toes should touch the floor. Do not force this, but allow gravity to do the pulling and stretching. The more you can relax your hips and spine, the more successful you will be. Advanced students can bring their arms back and touch their toes with their fingers. An easy way to work into the Plow is to bend your knees and rest them on your forehead with your arms clasped under your knees. Try to hold this position at least one minute.

Uncommonly supple people can bring their knees down on either side of their head and touch the floor with them.

The Plow is the lazy man's exercise par excellence and combines the benefits of stretching and inverted positions.

10. THE BRIDGE

From the Shoulderstand lower your legs down one at a time, to the floor in front, the opposite way from the Plow. Your arms are still supporting your back with your thumbs and fingers spread around your waist. Your legs are extended with your feet flat on the floor, so that your body forms an evenly curving arch.

11. THE DRAWBRIDGE

When you have mastered the Bridge, practice raising your legs one at a time back to the Shoulderstand. This variation we call the Drawbridge and it demands real proficiency. When you learn to go from Shoulderstand to Plow to Bridge and back again via the Drawbridge, you are well on the way to overcoming the inertial pull of gravity and making it work in your behalf.

The Bridge and Drawbridge are considered fairly advanced, but we include them because they stretch the spine in the opposite direction from the Plow. This completes a more challenging routine of forward and backward bending while in an inverted position.

12. NECK ROLLS

a. Allow your head to droop forward to your chest and leave it in this position, until you feel a pull at the back of your neck. Then inhale, and on one prolonged breath, rotate your head *slowly* all the way around, keeping your face turned to the front. Almost invariably beginners want to turn their face instead of allowing their head to droop and move freely. Repeat by rotating your head in the opposite direction. Don't be alarmed if you hear a grating or gritty sound as you move your neck. This demonstrates your need of the exercise. With practice it will eventually lessen or vanish completely.

b. Hang your head forward as before. Inhale while raising your head straight back and lifting your chin as high as possible. *Slowly* turn your face as far as you can around to the right. Then lower your chin down toward your right shoulder, touching it if possible. *Slowly* raise your chin back up on right, turn your face to the front and down again in the center. Your chin describes a wide arc from the base of your neck up, around, and down to your shoulder, then back again. Repeat on the left side. Continue until your neck begins to feel loose and supple and notice how your muscles progressively relax.

We have suggested doing Neck Rolls after the Shoulderstand, to counteract the extreme pressure on the neck, but actually they may be practiced any time and as often as possible. The first signs of aging often appear in the neck and chin, but this can be mitigated by slow deliberate stretching.

13. SITTING FORWARD BEND

Sit up straight and extend your arms with fingers pointed up and elbows straight. Raise them high over your head while breathing in. When you think you have stretched your arms as high as they can go, reach up a little farther and pull in with your lower back muscles. Exhale while bending slowly forward, reaching toward your toes, still stretching as far as possible. Keep your legs straight, even if this makes it harder to bend and endeavor to relax the muscles behind your knees. This will not be easy, but as you induce them to relax, you may find yourself bending further. Repeat two or three times.

The aim of this stretch is not to prove that you can touch your toes, but rather to demonstrate your ability to control and relax various sets of muscles. It is the ultimate in reverse effort — letting it happen rather than making it happen.

14. THE COBRA

Lie on your stomach with your palms on the floor at shoulder level, fingers pointed forward and your forehead touching the floor. The tips of your fingers should be in line with the top of your shoulders. Inhale and raise your head only. Follow with your upper chest. Finally raise your lower chest, keeping the lower part of your body on the floor from your navel down. Your elbows remain slightly bent. Look upward with your eyes as far as possible while raising your head and shoulders. Try to feel the successive parts of your spine moving in sequence as you raise and lower the top half of your body. Eventually the motion will feel fluid and snake-like. Exhale while coming down to the lying position. This exercise may be repeated up to seven times on the rhythm of the breath. A point to remember is that your elbows are never fully straightened, so that the pressure is exerted in bending the upper half of your back.

15. THE LOCUST

Lie prone on your stomach with hands at your sides, palms up, and your head resting on your chin. Inhale and raise your right foot, stretching it as far as possible up behind you, without bending your knee, and hold. Exhale and lower your leg. Repeat, using your other leg and keeping your face down. Continue, alternating legs, two or three times on each side.

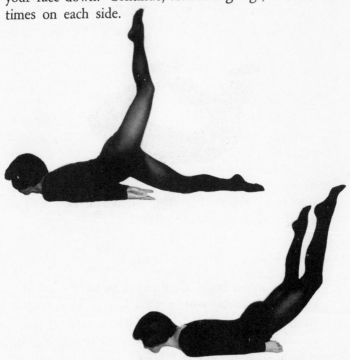

Advanced students can make this position more difficult by clenching their fists under their thighs and bringing both legs up with knees fairly straight, using a thrusting movement. Hold the legs high, as long as possible. This strengthens your lower back and pelvic region and brings an increased flow of blood to your head. The Locust is particularly beneficial because these lower supporting back muscles do not receive adequate stretching in the normal course of moving about.

16. THE BOW

Still lying on your stomach, bend your knees, reach back and grab your ankles with your hands and hold. Inhale and raise your head and feet as though trying to pull your knees up off the floor. Your arms should be taut like a bow-string. Advanced students can practice rocking forward and backward in this position. This combines the effects of the Cobra and Locust positions.

These positions follow Forward Bending because they stretch your spine in the reverse direction.

17. THE WAVE

Sitting on your heels, raise your hips up and forward to a kneeling position, with a wave-like or thrusting motion. Keep your arms at your sides. Repeat several times until you feel the rhythm of the movement rippling through your hips, back and shoulders.

18. THE HIP STRETCH

From a Heel Sitting position, stretch backward and rest with your arms straight, palms flat on floor, fingers forward. Those with supple backs can practice reclining back on their elbows or even with their shoulders touching the floor behind. The stretching of muscles which can be felt in your upper legs is beneficial for posture and for keeping your lower back straight and free. The Hip Stretch counteracts the tendency of the body to hunch with aging.

19. THE HIP LIFT

This insures that we leave no stone unturned, or stern untoned. In a Heel Sitting position with straight arms thrust backward, palms down, fingertips in line with your toes if possible, push straight down for support. Let your head sag back and raise your pelvis. Hold this position as long as comfortable. Advanced students can try to pull forward to a kneeling position, keeping hips raised and chest out, without using the arms or sagging in the middle.

20. THE TRIANGLE

Stand erect with your feet spread well apart. Extend your arms straight out to the sides at shoulder height, palms facing down, so that your body forms a cross. Breathe in and bend sidewards from your waist until one hand touches your ankle. The other swings up and over in a wide arc coming to rest alongside your ear, parallel to the floor, with your palm facing down. Be sure to stretch as far as possible with a straight elbow, so that your arm does not droop and all your limbs are taut. Hold from five to thirty seconds.

21. TRIANGLE TWIST

Stand as above, with feet well apart. Twist your head and torso around to the right, as far as possible. Then, bending from your waist with knees straight, clasp your right ankle with your left hand. Your left ear should be facing the floor. Now swing your right arm up until it rests on

your right ear, parallel to the floor, with elbow straight and palm facing down. Hold ten to thirty seconds and repeat, using the other side.

Doctors have found this oblique stretch extremely helpful in relieving menstrual problems.

22. THE ANKLE PULL

In a standing position inhale and raise your right foot behind you with bent knee. Grasp your right ankle with your right hand and pull your ankle up behind you. Your spine is erect and your left arm is extended straight upward. Try to stretch your back, as much as possible, by pushing your bent leg back as you pull up on your ankle with your hand. Aim at maintaining equilibrium rather than using any extreme bending motion. Repeat, using your left side.

You can warm up for the Ankle Pull by raising both arms high over your head while stretching your right leg in back of you. Repeat, using your left leg.

23. THE JACKKNIFE

Stand erect and inhale, stretching your arms high over your head and arch backward. Then bend forward slowly while exhaling, keeping your legs straight. Clasp your ankles with your hands and bring your face down toward your knees. Advanced people can touch their forehead to their knees. Try to hold a few seconds, then repeat. At the end of this position, stand for several seconds with your arms stretched as high as possible overhead and raise up on your toes.

In all of these exercises breathing should be exclusively through your nose. As a teacher of ours once put it, "The mouth is for eating and kissing the pretty girls. The *nose* is for breathing."

24. FLOATING

This has also been given the name of the Corpse, the Sponge, and "Collapsation." Collapsation expresses the state of collapse and relaxation you feel after exercising to your utmost. You have deliberately exhausted yourself, and now are ready to open up, accept and absorb the influx of healing forces which will re-create you in a new image of health. This is the reward you give your body for serving you so well.

Lie flat on your back with eyes shut and arms relaxed at your sides, palms up. As you slow down and deepen your breathing feel yourself being nourished by the oxygen and be thankful that you can have as much of it as you want without stint or limitation.

Visualize this nurturing energy flowing through whatever part of your body especially requires to be relaxed or healed. If, for example, your eyes are tired and ache, or your brain is fatigued, place your palms over closed eyelids, fingers resting on your forehead, and feel yourself inhaling through this area. The same gentle pressure of your hands may be applied to any aching place, or you can imagine the needful part being bathed in a stream of golden light as you soak up the vital atmosphere. Your whole body will seem more porous, permeable and pervaded with a delightful sense of well-being. The body in its wisdom can correct its malfunctions, but you must help supply the energy to stimulate cells and molecules in their efforts toward reconstruction.

Now gradually relax all your limbs, beginning with your toes and working up to your head. Feel your internal organs and tissues cooperating peacefully and bringing harmony to the whole. Appreciate the work that the body is accomplishing in your behalf. If you can be grateful and bless it, it will relax automatically.

Relax your mind also. Pretend you are taking a mental sunbath. Allow the radiant energies surrounding you to illumine your thoughts with images of light and beauty. Breathe in this shining substance of life until you feel buoyant and expansive, adrift on a shoreless sea of luminous splendor. Float far away on streaming iridescent tides, abandoned and free. . . .

Afterward, while still profoundly relaxed, implant the idea in your deeper psyche that, no matter what shadows dim this inner realm of light, you will still retain some measure of peace and clarity. In times of trial you will recall and find again the way back to the bright source and goal of all your striving, the quiet center where Peace is found.

Many people find it appropriate to close their relaxation period by repeating a final invocation. We suggest the following translation of an ancient prayer:

> May the energy of the divine self inspire me
> And the light of the soul direct.
> May I be led
> From darkness to light,
> From the unreal to the real,
> From death to immortality.
>
> *Peace, Peace, Peace* be unto all.
>
> OM   OM   OM

3

Tips on Exercising

1. Building your basic routine.

IF YOU HAVE TIME FOR ONLY ONE EXERCISE and wish to have an uplifting experience, try the Shoulderstand. It will do the most for you with the least effort.

Warm up to the Shoulderstand with Diaphragmatic Breathing and the Pump. Legs may be raised alternately, together, and with side-swinging motions, but always slowly with utmost stretching and control.

If you cannot accomplish the Shoulderstand or preliminary Inverted Posture, use a wall or bed to get your hips up off the floor. It has been said that "He who rests on his laurels must be wearing them in the wrong place." So let your foremost concern be to get the backmost part of yourself up and away from the too solid attraction of earth. Turning yourself topsy-turvy not only helps put the world in perspective but accomplishes the following results:

a. Your ancient foe, gravity, now becomes your friend and ally. Instead of being drawn inexorably down toward the ground (and ultimately all the way under), a process presaged by the tendency of fat to accumulate on the lower parts of the body, you are now ingeniously reversing the direction of pull. If you must sag, at least you will be sagging upward.

A little boy once said that women have hourglass figures

because as time passes they fall toward the bottom. So let it be "bottoms up" and time will flow backward as you feel younger day by day, and remove yourself from the category of steatopygic people.

b. Ponce de Leon traveled thousands of miles in quest of the Fountain of Youth, but we believe that it is as close as the bloodstream of your own body. The Shoulderstand, by stimulating circulation of the blood, gives life and youth to the weary. The brain comprises approximately one-fiftieth of your body's weight, yet burns one-fourth its oxygen supply. Oxygen is carried by your blood which, in this upside down position, increases in flow and pressure. This enables it to find new channels—collateral circulation—as well as to keep main arteries and veins elastic, reducing the possibility of cardio-vascular diseases. When the blood circulating through your brain follows the usual pathways your thinking, too, is bound to get into a rut. And when a rut goes deep enough, it is called a grave.

Proof of these brain-stimulating effects is found in several recent studies, comparing exercised and nonexercised rats. Those given a richly stimulating environment, with special trapezes and rat-tailored gymnastic equipment, turned out to have brains between four and five percent heavier than those kept in solitary cages. So revolutionary are the results of these studies that their implications may take years to be realized —but we can begin to act now.

c. Not only does the Shoulderstand cause your brain to be richly nourished with blood, but more nerve connections are made owing to its utilization of the entire body. Putting *all* of yourself into the effort leads to corresponding self-integration. Exercises produce as much benefit through coordination and stimulation of the nervous system, as through muscle building. You don't think just with your brain, but with every nerve in your body and the keenness of each one contributes to your overall self-awareness.

The ancient aphorism, "Mens sana in corpore sano," (a healthy mind in a healthy body) is as true today as ever. Studies at West Point have shown a correlation between academic failures and physical inferiority. At Phillips Academy in Andover, Massachusetts a dormitory of fifty boys was put on a program of midmorning exercises while another, set up as a control, had none. The active dormitory achieved twice as many classroom honors and half as many academic failures as the nonexercising group.

d. The Shoulderstand is the best position for regulating weight. It helps the overweight to reduce and the underweight to gain because it exerts pressure on the thyroid region of the neck and promotes extra circulation of the blood to this area. This exercise helps keep the glandular system in balance and brings the whole body into more efficient functioning order. Abdominal organs are not just squeezed in, but because the downward pressure of gravity is eliminated, the muscles are trained to hold them in their proper places.

In practice the Shoulderstand does cause excess fat to melt away, but for reasons that are as much psychological as physical. First, you become conscious of the effort of raising your hips from the ground and, second, anyone who spends the requisite minute or two in this position, contemplating a pendulous stomach (and there is nowhere else to gaze), is bound to want to do something about it. The position forces a facing up to yourself in every sense of the word.

The next additions to be made to the basic routine are forward and backward bends to help your spine become supple as well as strong. It has been said, "You are as young as your spine is flexible." Begin with Forward Bending and the Cobra; then add more challenging variations of the same kinds of stretches. The Plow, for example, is upside-down Forward Bending, while the Hip Lift reverses the Cobra.

Think in terms of the whole body, so that as many as possible of its more than six hundred muscles are utilized. Then, if you are going to ache, at least you will ache evenly all over and not excessively in one place! You will want to go on to side-bending and balancing postures, and can begin to experiment with those given in the appendix for advanced students. Do not be afraid to branch out with new and original forms of movement, but always try to end with one final upward stretch. It is always beneficial to begin and end any exercise session by reaching upward as far as possible in token of aspiration toward higher things. Then practice the final deep relaxation of Floating.

2. Standards of measurement.

Certain exercises provide a standard which you should regard as absolutely minimal and maintain as a matter of course. Merely continuing your routine will push you beyond old levels of achievement like the ancient Greek who started with a new-born calf and lifted it every day until it became an ox, and so became transformed into the strongest man in the country.

Positions in which you should acquire proficiency are Leg-raising, the Cat, Inverted Posture, Forward Bending, the Cobra and the ability to sit comfortably back on your heels. If you are relatively young and not able to do these things, then you are already tending toward trouble. Remember that when a doctor examines you he is limited in his ability to gauge your muscle tone, general coordination and elasticity, yet these are prime factors in staying fit. It is up to you to develop the resiliency which provides the foundation of good health.

Anyone middle-aged or under, and in fairly good condition, should be able to master the Shoulderstand, Plow, sitting Back-stretches, Locust and Bow, even if these require some time to accomplish. Lying on your back it should be possible to raise each knee and press it to your forehead with your hands. The essential factor is not muscular strength but flexibility and coordination in order to fully utilize existing resources.

Too many people are deluded into thinking brute strength is an end in itself. Sometimes when we held yoga classes, young men would come in who had been lifting weights without proper instruction. Already they were taking on a gorilla-like stance, with thick immobile necks, muscle-bound shoulders and legs, and a beefy red complexion. Yet the simplest stretching and bending exercises were beyond their capacity. One dreads to think what will happen to all that disused muscle as they lapse into middle age and demanding jobs, and fail to keep up their athletic discipline.

The exercises we are suggesting for your practice knit you together into the proper shape, making you hold your shoulders back, spine straight, stomach in and keeping your breathing deep and regular. You may not run a mile faster but you will walk many more of them.

Once you have set your own standard, you can relax as long as you measure up to it, and automatically upgrade your performance when you fall short. With this kind of thermostatic control you will be spared the anxiety of not knowing what to do for yourself, and the worse shock of suddenly discovering how far you have let yourself slide.

3. The "As-If" attitude.

Imagination is the quality which distinguishes man from the animals and enables him to reach beyond himself. It is a divine attribute capable of redeeming all others. If, therefore, you can't quite master an exercise, go right ahead and *imagine* yourself "as if" you were doing it perfectly.

Before beginning lie down flat, take a deep breath, and formulate your intent. Determine to give your utmost effort to the task so that you may call upon your deeper reserves. Afterward follow through with a thought-picture of yourself performing just a little bit better. The technique of evoking this extra power of the will adds a new dimension more potent than any number of superficial repetitions.

In studies made of basketball players, a group given extra practice improved twenty-four percent in goals made. A similar group which practiced *mentally,* imagining themselves going through the motions, improved twenty-three percent, while a third group which neither practiced nor visualized didn't improve at all. If you can think ahead and follow through in imagination, you will find that not only do you perfect your performance, but the entire experience becomes more meaningful. You can use this technique to improve other accomplishments. You are not just learning exercises but learning how to learn.

4. When to eat.

The earliest recorded advice on this subject was given by Hippocrates, some 2,400 years ago. "Fat people who want to reduce should exercise on an empty stomach and sit down to the table while still out of breath." He was aware that exercise tends to depress the appetite at first, even though it may stimulate it later. Try, then, to do a few exercises before mealtime as a matter of habit.

Some fat people never exercise because they have been told that they should wait three hours after eating, and they are eating much of the time. But if you follow our admonition to snack or nibble, never consuming much, there is hardly an occasion when a little mild exercise is not beneficial. A diabetic is supposed to exercise after each meal to facilitate the entrance of glucose into the cell membranes because there isn't enough insulin to accomplish the job alone. Even for a perfectly healthy person, an after-dinner walk will help the body assimilate the sugar released into the bloodstream, burning off calories more efficiently.

Generally it is recommended that you wait a couple of hours after a meal for a real work-out, but our experience has been that individuals vary tremendously about this. One person would be in misery if as much as an apple had been eaten an hour before, while another could stand on his head right after dinner and feel fine. Most often the trouble was with the individuals who had allowed themselves to become too hungry. Those with hypoglycemia or low blood sugar (the opposite of diabetes) need to take special precautions and avoid long intervals between eating, or they may end up feeling burned out rather than invigorated. Because the brain requires so much glucose this condition of low blood sugar gives rise to mental symptoms of extreme nervousness and depression. The only rule we can give is to avoid hard-and-fast rules and discover your own requirements.

The main thing is not to allow mealtimes to become an excuse for undue delay and postponement. Adjust your eating habits to your exercise routine whenever possible, and not the other way around.

We do recommend some stretching exercises before breakfast, even if they are nothing more than glorified yawns. This is an excellent time for the gentle invigoration of breathing exercises. Just don't be dismayed to discover how stiff you are after a night's sleep. It shows how rapidly the body becomes immobilized when not used. Later in the day you will be surprised at the improvement.

Those able to plan their schedule can look forward to "exercise breaks" in the mid-morning and mid-afternoon as a welcome change in routine. Invite a friend to join you. This insures regularity and exertion of your best efforts, provided you save conversation until later. Play a classical record for atmosphere instead. Afterward reward your body for good behavior with a small treat.

Many people find evening the best time for exercise, but we do not recommend it after cocktails. For those who come to life in the late hours, the advantage of a workout before bedtime is that there is no deadline and sleep is improved. Not only is stretching inherently tranquilizing, but it cuts down midnight raids on the refrigerator, because your body is enabled to absorb glucose stored from dinner and so continues to "feed itself." Insomnia can also be overcome by getting up and putting your body through a strenuous workout. At least that will give you something positive to think about if yours is the sleeplessness caused by worry and anxiety. Some people lying awake at night count sheep, and some talk to the Shepherd, but some just need to bring their wandering thoughts back to the fold of their own deeper consciousness. The intense self-awareness involved in exercising magically distracts your thoughts from exacerbating cares and attunes your mind to your body's natural functions, of which sleep is the most basic.

5. Clothes.

We have tried to give exercises which can, for the most part, be done in ordinary clothes, but there is no questioning the fact that you will feel inspired when appropriately attired. Women find it helpful to get into the habit of wearing attractive slacks about the house, so that it is not necessary to change every time the impulse to do a Plow or Shoulderstand strikes. Those in northern climates sometimes wear leotards and tights under a skirt or jumper, to be ready for action. Several ladies who had fallen into this habit were surprised to find themselves becoming style-setters. Even their lethargic friends were appearing in bright leotards under suits or wrap-around skirts, and in stretch pants. No doubt they were helped, since in such an outfit the urge to move extravagantly becomes almost irresistible. Those whose weight disallows tights can try culottes which can be bought, or made from an ordinary full skirt.

6. Elimination.

Do not be surprised if, at the start of your new exercise regime, you find yourself making frequent trips to the bathroom. This is part of the general purging process and shows that the body is responding to the new discipline. If you have been in the laxative habit, this is a fine time to shake it for good.

7. Resistance.

It is important for you not to worry if your daily workout doesn't seem to make you look or feel much better for a while.

Occasionally people feel temporarily worse, and this is one reason why there is so little follow-through. Like pouring clear water into a muddy stream all the poisons and toxins in the system are churned up before being carried off. This is especially true of smokers who may cough and choke as breathing exercises dislodge the tar and nicotine in their lungs and blow it into the system.

Perfection brings imperfection to the surface, and so you are likely to feel worse before you feel better, unless already in good condition. You may ache in muscles you didn't even know you had, but you will toughen and gain endurance. Mother Nature is infinitely forgiving. At least you are becoming aware of your limitations and so are in a position to remove them. As Freud wrote, "If we can not see clearly, at least we can learn to see the obscurities clearly."

The real problem is that minor physical reactions will trigger far more obdurate psychological resistances. Excuses for not exercising are apt to be excuses for avoiding self-confrontation and are as varied as the imagination can fabricate. The mind will seize on slight indispositions and magnify them to immense proportions and in any treacherous way possible persuade you that some other task is of more immediate importance than your fifteen-minute-workout.

Some real fatigue and even nausea may be felt at the start because an unusual proportion of your energies is being diverted to the task of inner reconstruction. The sensation is akin to that "washed out" feeling that accompanies pregnancy or convalescence. Only instead of creating a new body you are re-creating your own. Wait about nine months, approximately a season, for the emergence of the new you.

Learn to be tough without forcing. Each one must discover the razor-thin margin between pushing beyond old limitations and just plain over-doing. The confidence resulting from trusting your own powers of judgment is as important as the confidence and power that comes from being able to do the exercises. This self-reliant attitude counters the dependency that manifests itself as overindulgence in food and drink.

Allow muscles and nerves to indicate what they can do, how far you can go, and when you should stop, even while you continue to assert your mastery of mind and will. The effect should be that of a dialogue, not you forcing and the body fighting back, but a situation of mutual cooperation and respect.

8. Integrating the routine into your life.

As you become more creatively "lazy" you may take up the challenge to think up new ways of increasing your exercise benefits with less expenditure of time and effort. Any way you can enliven your routine with soft music, incense, a special practice mat, or an attractive place for retreat, is recommended. You can also gear exercise to other activities. Sitting down can be a signal to practice pulling in your stomach while expelling your breath. Drinking a cup of coffee or tea can trigger a reaction of slowing down and deepening your breathing. While waiting for people, put your hands behind your neck and stretch backward as far as possible. Other conditioners are:

TV WATCHING

Make it a point to sit on the floor while you watch television. Then, without even trying, you will benefit from moving your legs around in different positions. Practice sitting on, and between, your feet. Place the soles of your feet together in front of you and bend forward over them, bringing your forehead toward the floor. Try Alternate Breathing, Neck Rolls, and Hip Lifts.

DRIVING

Waiting in the car affords an opportunity to work on neck exercises, which will enable you to swing your head around with ease when you have to check traffic behind you. Practice squeezing the wheel, pressing your shoulder blades together and working on your stomach muscles. If you have any degree of privacy work on your face and scalp muscles. Commuting offers an excellent opportunity to make deep breathing a regular routine.

TELEPHONING

Try standing on one leg and tense the muscles of the thigh and buttock while you are talking on the telephone. Make sure that the arm of the hand holding the receiver is not tense. Much stiffness of the neck and shoulders could be alleviated if those who do business on the telephone would try using their other hand for a change. Not only would it relieve their telephone arm, but it would alert them to the extent that their mental tensions are being translated into physical inflammation and stiffening. Depending on your interest in the conversation and your powers of concentration, you can add to your telephone repertoire, until even the teen-agers in your household will be surprised at your agility.

SITTING

Not long ago a well-known professional writer was obliged to undergo major surgery to correct a paralysis in both arms. "It was an occupational disability," he shrugged. "It came from forty years of bending over a typewriter."

This kind of fatalism seems to us sad and unnecessary, because every writer has to sit back occasionally and think about what he has to say. These times are good for stretching and moving the arms and upper back in various ways, rotating the shoulders, the palms of the hands and squeezing back with the elbows or wide-spread arms.

Practice pulling in your lower back when you are at a desk or table and notice how your shoulders automatically straighten. Bad posture begins not so much in the shoulders, as in the hunching which occurs at the lower end of the spine as supporting muscles shrink into flabby disuse. If the foundation is right the rest of the back and neck will naturally fall into correct alignment. Try to practice sitting straight, with arms stretched as high over the head as possible, elbows straight and palms together (the Mountain). Hold them that way until they start to ache.

A way to check your posture is to sit on the floor, legs outstretched in front, and press your back against the wall. There should be no gap between the base of your spine and the wall. Then raise arms high over your head so that your fingers touch one another or barely interlock. Continue pressing your elbows and hands against the wall. Breathe deeply and feel the straight line of your back and spine.

READING

This exercise is especially helpful if you read in bed. It can also be practiced on a carpet. Lie on your stomach and prop the book or magazine you are reading in front of you, so that in effect you are doing the Cobra.

IN BED

Practice lying on your back with your hands clasped behind and above your head. Raise your knees, keeping the soles of your feet on the sheet. Then bring your knees down slowly, all the way on the right, while turning your head the opposite way, to the left. Reverse, by bringing your knees down to the left and looking to the right, so that your spine twists from top to bottom.

Practice stretching your legs, tensing and relaxing separate muscles, and lying flat on your stomach with your arms extended out and upward on the pillow. Many people will be able to think of even more interesting exercises to enliven their time in bed.

9. Inspire others.

In the beginning your friends, and especially your family, may scoff or make what they consider amusing remarks about your new routine. You may have to resign yourself to the fact that although they would be full of loving sympathy if you were sick, your efforts to attain a higher level of wellness have them baffled or even resentful — unless of course you are blessed with unusually understanding relations. Until you have established yourself and are experiencing some real improvement, it may be better just to keep your mouth shut.

Then, once you have proved something to yourself, a little missionary work is in order. Persuade some friends to join you and teach them what you have discovered for yourself. Not only will this afford continued incentive, but you will learn an immense amount from the good and bad examples of others. Even with good friends keep it basically serious. Don't clown or fool around or you will ruin everything.

As you become more sensitive to the actions and reactions of your own body you will find yourself responding more keenly to others. You will perceive their needs and want to help them, even as you are being helped. Assert your better instincts and be the giver. Somehow, in some way, find another person to assist, because once you have started teaching, you will really begin to learn.

PART THREE

The Breath of Life

1

The Vital Breath

THE MIND OF MAN IS LIKE A FLAME. The body is the fuel on which it feeds. Just as the presence of air makes all burning possible, so the rhythmic flow of the breath brings together flesh and spirit, rendering each one sensible in terms of the other.

This organic combustion, which transmutes the dull matter of the body into the variegated light of consciousness, regulates every aspect of behavior. Consider what happens to the flame of a candle covered by a glass. It flickers and dies. So, too, each cell of your body must consume oxygen to convert its food into the vital force which supports all higher functions. If the cells are oxygen-starved, this essential metabolic process is not accomplished. Instead of being released as energy, the remnants of our meals are stuffed away into "dead storage" (usually around the hips and belly) where the fat is unavailable for use regardless of need.

"I'm starving!" This bitter plaint of the overweight person arises from no mere delusion in the mind. Indeed, there is more of him to be hungry. But a better word would be suffocating. His excess poundage sets up a vicious circle whereby the mechanical motions of respiration are impeded, there is not sufficient oxygen to supply his bulk, and inadequate circulation can not transport the diminished amount of oxygen to famished tissues. By contrast the thin person will pick away at his food, often leaving his plate half full. This is not necessarily a sign of fortitude as much as his good fortune to be naturally slender and better able to utilize his bodily resources.

Deep breathing alone may not reduce weight, but it will help return the extra supply of fat to "live storage" where it can be burned. The energy will then be provided that stimulates the whole system to activity, arousing extra incentive to diet and become more attractive or virile. Starving as a method of reducing may produce results initially, but seldom does it remove pounds proportionately; and it can hardly ever be carried on long enough to eliminate the obdurate layers of "hard fat" which make the difference between flabbiness and firmness. Instead the body burns less. Deep breathing and diet are ultimately effective only in combination, just as a boiler must be regulated by adjusting air intake to fuel supply.

Your body ingests two kinds of substances, food and air. The former enters through your mouth, the latter through your nose. The subtle nourishment of the atmosphere is as essential as the gross nourishment of food. This is evidenced by the fact that most people can live for weeks without eating, days without drinking, but hardly four minutes without breathing. When fatigued it is not a big meal that refreshes as much as sleep or exercise, both of which induce deeper respiration.

There are five fundamental considerations to be taken into account by the individual who embarks on a determined weight-control program. These, in order of increasing importance, are (1) Diet, (2) Exercise, (3) Deep Breathing, (4) Relaxation and (5) Creative Visualization. The methods included under each of these headings involve more than just coping with physical disabilities. They enhance the entire personality. It is not enough to be merely well adjusted or "normal." The ordinary man's desire to be extraordinary is a divine quality and the hope of the world. Now, as never before, we have urgent need to experiment with techniques for higher development and for releasing powers which will see the emergence of a type of human being representative of a new, more evolved kingdom on earth, as superior to man as man is to the animals. This quest for self-realization we call yoga, or union.

Too many people are like the man who shuffled into his doctor's office and sighed, "Gee! Doc, I hope I'm sick because I'd sure hate to feel this way if I were well." Positive health is no mere absence of disease but a vital and ever growing capacity to utilize inner resources and radiate healing strength and encouragement to others.

The five-fold program described above can be meaningful only when all its aspects are interrelated with regard to a total plan of action. In order to remember them think of a loaf of bread. *Diet* represents the basic ingredients, milk, flour, eggs, butter, or whatever raw materials are selected for flavor and nutrition. It also regulates the proportions supplied. *Exercise* is the mixing and kneading which blends these substances and facilitates their smooth interaction. *Deep Breathing* is the yeast leavening the entire loaf. *Relaxation* allows time for the dough to grow light and rise, while *Creative Visualization* is the fire which transforms the raw foodstuff into the staff of life.

Our earthly existence begins and ends with the breath, and controlled respiration provides the key to the effectiveness of the above mentioned functions. Our very first decision is whether to "holler or swaller," that is, whether to breathe out or breathe in. From then on the working parts of the body receive their payment in oxygen, without which all are impoverished. Breathing also inspires our participation in the larger economy of nature, enriching us with a sense of the abundance of life which is our common birthright.

The outline below indicates the varied effects we discuss in this and subsequent chapters. Controlled breathing produces:

1. Oxygenation of the blood . . Physical revivification
2. Imposition of a new rhythm . . Emotional regulation
3. Deliberate autosuggestion   . . .   Mental relaxation
4. Direction of the vital forces . Spiritual regeneration

To begin with the physical — we have already pointed out the necessity for pumping an adequate supply of oxygen into the bloodstream. In order to admit oxygen the lungs must work in cooperation with muscles of the stomach and diaphragm. This synchronization is quite simple in practice, providing you have some understanding of the basic theory involved.

DIAPHRAGMATIC BREATHING

*Permit your stomach to relax and move outward while inhaling,
and to contract while exhaling.*

Think of your lungs as being roughly pyramidal in shape.
Not only are they broadest and most capacious at the bottom,
but there they have ample space to expand and swell downward, whereas the upper part is increasingly bound in by ribs.

Diaphragmatic Breathing can be practiced in any position,
but is most beneficial when lying flat on a rug or firm surface
with your hands resting on your solar plexus, directly above the
navel, so that the up and down motion of your abdomen can
be plainly felt. Let your stomach balloon out as the breath is
drawn in, and contract, pushing all the air out from below,
during exhalation. This superbreathing should be practiced
after exercising, so that oxygen reserves may be replenished.
It also helps you summon up the energy for new endeavors.
Any time you are momentarily stymied, stop and breathe! This
will prime the pump and ready you for action.

A fat friend of ours hit upon the pump priming psychology
in his response to suggestions that he might keep his weight
down if he would only try exercising.

"Whaddya' mean I don't exercise!" he retorted. "Every
morning first thing I begin. Up — down, up — down, up —
down. Then after three strenuous minutes of this I say, 'OK
fella, now we'll try the other eyelid'."

The next stage would be to coordinate the ups and downs
with deep breathing, adding leg raising, arm stretching and
neck rolling. With luck he might even emerge from bed to try
the Elephant. The body wants to go on to more challenging
assignments once stirred from its lethargy. But if asked to
start jumping around violently in the early hours of the
morning it will rightfully protest.

Eventually Diaphragmatic or, as it is often called, Abdominal Breathing, becomes so habitual that the initially exagger-

ated motion of the stomach gives way to a gentle relaxation of the muscles, allowing the diaphragm to descend and air to be sucked in all the way to the bottom of the lungs, without visible distention. In this exercise the shoulders must not be raised at all but remain relaxed, while the upper chest hardly moves. Plenty of air circulates through the top in any event, but with Diaphragmatic Breathing all parts of the lungs are cleaned out.

Many weight-watching women object to this uninhibited breathing because they fear that permitting their already sagging stomachs to expand would make them appear still more protuberant. They would rather buttress themselves with corsets until, as the years pass, they thicken into an indistinguishably tubular stance, backside compressed into the "monobuttock" and stomach shoved up around the waist, obliterating all youthful feminine contours, save for an exaggerated bosom spilling over the top. At the other end, thighs constricted by girdles with tourniquet legs, bulge into pillars of varicosities encased in elastic stockings ending in swollen ankles and puffy feet, squeezed, as a final indignity into tiny shoes.

Men, despite their nooses of ties, collars and belts are better disposed toward the idea of "belly breathing" and so fare more happily. It is indeed a pathetic irony that the concern for shape which keeps many women so tightly held in below is actually instrumental in ruining both figure and disposition. Fewer supports would supply the incentive to develop a do-it-yourself girdle of muscle bands and to stand firm and free. In "keeping the chin up" and "stiffening the backbone" we gain strength to meet the world, not by hiding out behind stiff bone or elastic disguises.

Holding in the stomach with tight rigidity manifests no real control, as much as a culturally warped repression of what goes on below the diaphragm. Victorian ladies were supposed never to mention the word "leg" but referred delicately to something known as a "limb." This was the age of the tightest of all waist binders, as though by cutting off their upper half they could deny everything going on in the nether regions of the body. Little wonder they were prostrated by vapors, swooning, hysteria and other vague indispositions. The resultant pallor, heaving of the bosom and languor, was evidently considered romantic.

Recently a friend told us his doctor suggested he contain his bulging bay window by imagining someone was continually holding a knife to his stomach. It seemed a negative way to produce positive results. We suggested an exercise routine, starting with deliberate "feeding" of the offending area with large drafts of air, inhaled to the very depths of his body, until the instinct for restraint revived and took over naturally. Perhaps this is how yogis gain the reputation for contemplating their navel, since the solar plexus controls the lower centers. Diaphragmatic Breathing helps keep the whole body in good running order with muscles toned and nerves in tune. It is the flywheel regulating all moving parts.

The objection is sometimes raised that Diaphragmatic Breathing seems unnatural. An initial sense of awkwardness shows that people have disregarded their instincts for so long that they fail to realize this is really nature's way. It is the efficient method spontaneously adopted by children, primitive people, animals and by everyone during relaxed hours of sleep. If you have a cat, notice how first the lower section of its abdomen swells out, then the upper to complete the breath.

The most important point to remember is that *it is more important to breathe out than in.* Little good is accomplished by sucking up an enormous gulp of fresh air if all you are doing is pushing the old, stale air deeper into the cavities at the base of the lungs where it stagnates or overdistends delicate lining membranes. Notice how overweight persons gasp and heave for breath, often becoming barrel-chested in self-defeating efforts to fill up.

Your lungs are a sponge. To fill this sponge it must first be squeezed. When released, innumerable small compartments bounce back into shape and suck in needed replenishment. This squeezing effect not only forces out all the tired air but maintains the elasticity and absorbency of lung tissue. Exercising the lungs increases resistance to infectious and respiratory ailments.

Some people have trouble breathing correctly, even when they know the technique, because their abdominal muscles have become too weak to do the job. They tend to raise their shoulders and end with stiff necks and aching backs. But if your diaphragm, with its capacity to rise and fall several inches and exert a broad upward push, is trained along with the lower supporting muscles, good breathing will naturally result. The following exercise insures that you do not work against yourself by trying to inhale with the top of the lungs while clamping in with the stomach muscles below.

THE STOMACH LIFT

To accomplish the Stomach Lift exhale completely and draw in your stomach while the air is entirely out of your lungs. If properly performed you will feel a strong pull at the base of your neck due to the vacuum created in your lungs. When you have learned to suck your stomach *in* on the outbreath, as though to press your navel against your backbone—then endeavor to raise your diaphragm up under your rib cage. Try to raise and lower it successively three to five times before inhaling. These are two different motions; first, in and out; and second, lifting and lowering your diaphragm.

The Stomach Lift forces you to develop and manipulate the diaphragm, squeezing out old air and keeping the base of the lungs elastic. It firms up your internal muscles, massages vital organs and powerfully stimulates nerves and glands.

When respiration has long been inadequate, particularly in the case of smokers, the bottom of the lungs begins to resemble a swamp. Fluid accumulates, stagnates, and disease germs flourish. Soggy membranes lose their resiliency. The body fights futilely to overcome the spreading flaccidity with rapid, irregular and shallow spurts of breath. This condition is called emphysema, the Greek word for inflation.

The problem of emphysema is not just that it has reached epidemic proportions, but that from its inception, usually unrecognized, it devalues the whole currency of our physiological economy. Anyone who has experienced discomforting shortness of breath should ask what value life can have if it is impossible to enjoy the unlimited bounty of the atmosphere. Because the air is free we fail to realize that it is priceless.

While emphysema is irreversible in its later stages, it is entirely preventable by methods requiring neither time, money nor skill. Gulping pills and inhaling bottled oxygen are but stop-gasp measures, though smoking should immediately and unequivocally be renounced by anyone with incipient emphysema. Many things are good smoked, such as cheese and fish, but definitely not human lungs.

As with economic inflation the process of emphysema is self-perpetuating, a vicious spiral to disaster. The sufferer struggles to catch his breath only to find that it eludes him. Frantic inhalation breaks down delicate cell walls of the lungs leaving less absorbing surface, like blowing the connecting partitions out of adjacent rooms. The more that is taken in, the less can be given out, and the capacity of the lungs to soak up oxygen is inexorably diminished.

Curiously enough, the spread of emphysema reflects global factors which underlie much of the malaise of society today. It is not only our lungs that inflate uselessly. Bodies, world populations, economies, bombs, possessions, information in our minds, the sum of available knowledge, all seem to be undergoing a vast disorderly proliferation. This is not coordinated growth improving quality, but a cancerous spread and accumulation of accumulations, with no unifying scheme or central principle to give significant worth to the aggregate. Productivity is not creativity until subsumed to some integrative purpose.

This "bigger is better" philosophy is reminiscent of the street musician who started out with a modest hand organ and a monkey to collect pennies in a tin cup, and who ultimately became such a resounding success that he was able to acquire a pipe organ and a gorilla!

In contrast to this emphasis on growth for its own sake, is the ineptness with which modern man tends to handle everything involving the art of letting go, beginning with this originating mode of breathing out. Yet the most essential life processes demand an ability to relax and have faith in nature's wisdom. Being born, dying, sexual union, giving birth, nursing a baby, sleep, elimination, all require the least possible interference from the conscious ego. On a social level, issues of allowing our children, other people and nations to be free to develop in their idiosyncratic ways, without spying, bugging, or otherwise meddling in their affairs, have become raging controversies in an authoritarian world.

Consider a modern individual, born with forceps and drugs, toilet trained with suppositories until the laxative habit takes hold, craving alcohol to become sufficiently uninhibited to make love or dance, taking tranquilizers to relax, pills to sleep, and dying finally in a drug induced stupor. Eventually nothing that has to do with release or elimination seems right or nice.

This is the attitude of the prim governess in charge of a small girl who came in from play one morning exclaiming that it was so hot she was sweating. "My dear," the governess said reproachfully, "horses sweat, men perspire, but ladies merely glow!"

Is it any wonder then, that people have trouble eliminating excess fat from their bodies and construct an array of psychological resistances to dieting! Such renunciation rubs against the grain of all subconscious fears of letting go (solidly implanted since infancy) until the very flesh fights to conserve its gains.

Those who go through life forever struggling against the dictates of nature are like shipwreck victims thrashing and flailing about, instead of adapting to the water and floating. The same element they fight as an enemy could hold them up and save them. To sur-vive means literally to rest on top of life. Our endeavor is not to deny but to accept and draw our sustenance from deeper levels of our being like the lotus whose roots are nourished by the muck below, in order that it may float unsullied in the sun and air.

People often ask if they are too old or too ill to exercise. The answer is that if you can breathe there is something constructive you can do. If rigor mortis has set in the chances are not so good — but even young people can be afflicted with rigor mortis of the mind.

Singing and reading aloud can be effective breathing exercises and explain in part why going to church can be uplifting. Yawning, laughing, whistling, humming, even talking, overcome lethargy by pumping more oxygen into your system. Anyone, however heavy, elderly or stiff, is going to have to keep on breathing, like it or not, and so can begin right here where life itself begins.

ISOMETRIC EXERCISES

Once you have learned to breathe diaphragmatically Isometric Exercises involving stretching and tensing of the various parts of the body can prove efficacious, even for those who can indulge in nothing more strenuous than reaching out an arm or leg. You can't get hurt just by stretching, but you can be helped.

Inhale deeply, extend your arms and tense them tightly while holding your breath. Then allow them to fall down and relax at your sides, exhaling slowly and completely. Repeat with the legs, neck and as many muscles of the body as you can deliberately control. Alternate stretching, tensing and relaxing.

If you are totally incapacitated concentrate on the act of breathing, while visualizing the accompanying motions in your mind. Although the movements may be only imaginary the breathing roots them in your nervous system where they will have their effect. Above all, keep on trying.

Isometric Exercises not only tone your body but release nervous tension by making it work for instead of against you. Like breathing routines they produce a subtle electrification of your nervous system inspiring further progress. As you evolve an increasing fund of volitional energy you become like an investor who plows his dividends back into buying more stock, pyramiding his investment to yield increasing returns.

We can only suggest these time-tested techniques. The main part of the therapy lies in your own thoughtful application of those methods which can benefit you personally. The dependency on food which causes some individuals to become fat often gives them a peculiar resistance to exercising alone, without a guru or teacher to stand over them and explain every detail. This should not be necessary. Any truly effective program must eventually become a "do-it-yourself" system, since it concerns the body you own, and your own life. That is what self-realization means; to be able to discover and use the powers in yourself, by yourself. It has to be up to you.

2

Breath,
The Rhythm of Being Alive

WHEN YOU ARE NERVOUS, UPSET, OR EXCITED, your breath is apt to shake your whole body with rapid, irregular and jerky motions. Your chest shudders, neck tenses and shoulders constrict. The more urgent your efforts to gasp in air, the more spasmodic the effect. The result is an oppressive incoordination and feeling of confusion. Sometimes serenity can be restored by deliberately slowing down your breathing, or by enjoying the refreshing rhythm of a walk.

The association of breath with mental attitude can be demonstrated by a brief experiment. Concentrate on the second hand of your watch and resolve to think of nothing else until fifteen seconds have elapsed. Make this test with the idea that you will prove your ability to restrain the wanderings of your mind for a quarter of a minute. Do this before reading further.

What happened to your breathing? Almost certainly it slowed down or stopped. You can try the same experiment by concentrating on the effort of grasping your chair seat with your hands. The result will be the same. We must conclude that intense concentration causes your breathing rhythm to decelerate. Conversely, regular, slow breathing leads to a corresponding ability to concentrate your physical and mental forces.

There are correlations between the stress which causes breathing and glandular action to be irregular, and the habitual tension which is manifested in disproportionate motion, shape, ambition and moods. Dieters tend to go on binges, then punish themselves with starvation. They stuff at night, and skip breakfast. Weight levels swing sporadically up and down. As one overly voluptuous girl sighed, "Since I started my diet I have lost a thousand pounds."

One reason why dancing can be so beneficial for heavy people is that it instills a basic sense of rhythm, grace and endurance which encourages a general desire for harmony. Most dancers retain their firm figures right into old age, along with an enthusiasm for living. The rhythm of the sea is also soothing to many people and a cruise is traditionally an antidote for nervousness and fatigue. There is something about going back to the sea from whence we all came, with its measured splash of surf and myriad dancing waves, that heals the troubled spirit. An overweight lady we know had a swing hung from the ceiling of her living room and entertains her friends while swaying serenely back and forth. Old-fashioned rocking chairs will also be popular as long as people continue to be plagued with old-fashioned back pains and stiffening joints. Rhythm, like breathing, is a stirring of the life force seeking expression through the manifold forms of creation.

The saying that "the breath is the life" is echoed in many languages, and this breath is always identified with the soul or essence of man. The Latin "spiritus" and "anima," the Greek "pneuma," the Hebrew "nepesh" and "ruakh," and the Sanskrit "prana" all show how, from early times, breath has been experienced as the moving spirit of existence. In the story of creation the Bible says, "And the Lord God formed man of the dust of the ground, and He breathed into his nostrils the breath of life; and man became a living soul."

An Eastern tradition holds that every individual is destined to draw just so many breaths during the course of his years on earth. If he can slow down his rate of respiration then he will last longer. Some yogis and holy men have endeavored to accomplish this and their longevity is legendary. We believe that the beneficial effects of slow breathing on health and disposition do, indeed, prolong years. In general, people who live in the mountains, such as the Hunzas, seem to endure longer than those on the plains who need not develop their lungs to obtain the necessary air.

Slow-breathing creatures such as tortoises, snakes and elephants live longer than such extremely rapid-breathing animals as rabbits, mice and shrews. The monkey's rate of thirty times a minute is nearly twice that of a human, but less than a rat, which breathes sixty times a minute, or a canary's one hundred and eight breaths a minute. On the other hand, a horse will breathe only about twelve times a minute and a tortoise scarcely more than three. The slow-breathers are also less nervous and jumpy.

The archetypal act of breathing reminds us that the rhythm of creation is composed of alternating phases. The Chinese have a saying that when a thing goes as far as it can in one direction, it turns around and becomes its opposite. The inbreath gives way to the outbreath and by this rhythm our bodies are inextricably linked with the primordial ebb and flow of all existence. As long as we breathe we are participants in nature's stately ritual of days and nights, growth and decay, waxing and waning moons, rising and falling tides, venous and arterial circulation, positive and negative electrical pulsations.

To breathe rhythmically is natural. Any disequilibrium or imbalance in the psyche will be expressed by a disturbance in respiration which will, in turn, feed back into nervous tension and physical disproportion to throw everything out of kilter again. Regular breaths should be like neat stitches fitting together the seams of body and mind to make a suitable garment for the soul.

The psychiatrist, Alexander Lowen, discovered that patients who seem afraid to exhale fully, but continually endeavor to swell out their chests, are often neurotically afraid to let go. Deep-seated fears prevent them from relinquishing this puffed-up attitude (sometimes accompanied by a puffed-up ego with its inevitable propensity to deflation and depression). Because of this inner emptiness they are compelled to construct rigid defenses. Their sense of insufficiency is translated into an armor-plated attitude of physical rigidity and emotional resistance.

It often happens that such people experience intense panic when they are induced to move and breathe correctly. One must work through layers of psychological resistance to effect their release. They are afraid to give in to the new rhythm, as though to "let go" meant to "make stop." They seem to fear that life would cease without their manipulating the machinery. Sometimes their conduct becomes so interfering that one wonders what God did before they were born.

A whole constellation of repressive attitudes accounts for the fact that many people, especially women, refuse to try Diaphragmatic Breathing, protesting that to relax will spoil their figures. It is not that they don't care, but that they care too much to let go of their defenses and show their vulnerability. Their emptiness within demands the appearance of solidarity.

Almost anyone can drop a few pounds without much trouble, but when overweight people try to lose a lot of weight they frequently become seriously depressed. The problem is that no one can lose pounds permanently without relinquishing the attitudes which caused the gain in the first place. They announce their good intentions and really mean them, but there is still something that is *afraid* to let the pounds go. How many have protested, "I would like to lose X number of pounds, but I wouldn't want to be *too* thin," when actually the chance of their being thin is the thinnest thing they will ever have. Some inkling of this resistance can be seen in their anxious attitude toward their slender children or relatives, whom they are apt to consider undernourished.

People who are overweight blame their doctors for not giving them adequate counsel, and encouragement with dieting. But the busy physician knows from long experience that, do what he may, obesity is so ingrained a condition he might as well conserve his strength for those he can help. He can salve his conscience with the thought that even psychiatrists don't achieve much success in dealing with weight problems.

All too often the would-be dieter is like a certain wayfarer who went staggering about under an immense pack. A sympathetic observer asked him what he was carrying and found that the burden contained nothing more than rusty junk scavenged along the road. "Why do you haul all this useless stuff around with you?" the friend asked. "I can't help it," the wayfarer replied. "It's all I've got."

In contrast with the inflated or "neurotic" types of inbreathers are certain types of schizoid personalities who, as described by Lowen, show a tendency to keep their lungs permanently deflated. Their chests appear hollow or concave and their shoulders are rounded as though to ward off the slings and arrows of outrageous fortune. They give the impression of trying to return to the fetal position. To breathe is, above all, to be alive, to burn, desire, expand and participate in the great chain of being, and no one who shares the air can escape this common destiny. The basic anxiety of the schizoid temperament is betrayed in slackness of muscle tone, looseness of gait, and inability to care, even about their own noncaring. Frequently they reject food which, like air, is a symbol of partaking in life, and they must be fed forcibly.

ALTERNATE BREATHING

Recognizing the profound link between rhythmic respiration and spiritual inspiration, the yogis of India long ago developed an exercise known as "Alternate Breathing," which helps tranquilize the entire personality. This is possibly the most commonly practiced of all yoga techniques and is considered the safest and the best. It has always been known in the East and is rapidly gaining popularity in Europe and America. The method is as follows:

Using your right hand, hold the thumb up, the next two fingers down against the palm, and the last two up. Practice pressing the thumb on your right nostril and then the last two fingers together against your left nostril, until you have acquired the knack of being able to stop the breath, first on one side and then on the other. Inhale on the left while pressing the right nostril with your thumb. Then exhale on the right while closing the left nostril with the last two fingers. Then inhale on the right and exhale on the left, closing off your nostrils as before. Repeat.

Always inhale on the same side from which you have just exhaled.

As soon as you have familiarized yourself with the basic holding technique, add a counting rhythm. Inhale for four seconds on the left, and exhale eight on the right. Then inhale four on the right, and exhale eight on the left. Repeat. Exhalation always takes twice as long as inhalation because it is more important to breathe out than to breathe in, squeezing the lungs like a sponge. If you have difficulty exhaling the full eight counts, keep on pulling your stomach muscles in and press them up against the base of your lungs as described in the Stomach Lift.

Now add a middle or holding interval. Inhale four counts on the left side, hold four, and exhale eight counts on the right. Then inhale four counts on the right, hold four, and exhale eight on the left. While holding, gently press your nostrils closed from both sides. This is one round, and rounds may be repeated from three to five minutes or more.

The middle or holding interval can gradually be increased to eight, twelve or sixteen, according to proficiency. Traditionally a ratio of one/four/two was considered ideal. That is, you should work up to a rhythm of four counts for inhaling, sixteen for holding, and eight for exhaling.

There is no need to try and prove your ability to hold your breath. The qualities to cultivate are relaxation, rhythm and ease. Yoga students sometimes raise the count as high as eight/thirty-two/sixteen, but they are developing endurance for special purposes.

It is important that you concentrate on the straightness of your back. Think of your body as a dynamo, and your spine as a conducting rod through which pulse electrical currents generated by your breathing. If the vertebrae are out of alignment these forces can not flow freely because they seep out or are deflected. Performing the Alternate Breathing exercise correctly, with the requisite straight spine, is one way to cultivate a sensitivity to the interplay of these subtle physiological energies.

Yoga exercises, called *asanas* (pronounced ah'-sa-nas), were originally developed to keep the back straight and strong, in order that the body might serve as an adequate container for forces invoked by deep breathing and meditation. The emphasis placed on the flexibility of hip and knee joints, enabling the practitioner to sit cross-legged in the Lotus posture for hours at a time, insured the upright position necessary to permit the psychic forces to rise from the base of the spine into the head through an unimpeded channel. The word "asana" literally means seat or position, but has been generalized to include the 840,000 positions of Hatha Yoga, only a few of which are considered fundamental. These we have included in our exercise sections. It seems significant that, in the East, taking an asana or position implies a seated posture of meditation, while in the West a position is something for which one actively "stands."

Students practicing Alternate Breathing frequently find it more troublesome than anticipated. This is not because they can't consciously hold the breath, but because in an obscure way the new rhythm clashes with the old. Not realizing that the unsettling effect comes because their basic body chemistry is involved, they rationalize their failure to follow through by telling themselves it is silly or boring.

With persistence the effects of Alternate Breathing prove remarkably tranquilizing. The psychological benefits produced may relate to the fact that yogic breathing can increase the carbon dioxide content of the blood and alveolar tissue in the lungs, resulting in increased pressure of carbon dioxide gas upon the nerve cells in the brain. Carbon dioxide has been used therapeutically in modern psychiatry and, in specific concentrations, has been proven to have a restorative power on the individual nerve cell. Dr. Meduna, a contemporary psychiatrist, who developed the technique of having patients inhale a mixture of thirty percent carbon dioxide and seventy percent oxygen, claims that a series of such treatments has restored extremely neurotic individuals to a stable, relaxed, and productive condition. He has written a book on the subject called *Carbon Dioxide Therapy.*

The effect of the carbon dioxide treatment is one of introspectiveness and self-awareness. This is similar to the state produced by the shaman when inhaling the smoke of resinous conifers, the Tibetan oracles when they breathed incense, and the Delphic oracle when she inhaled the vapors rising from fissures in the ground.

Some people are greatly concerned because they have been told that breathing exercises are dangerous and produce premature unfoldment of psychic powers. Some oversensitization of the nervous system can occur, but only when the exercises are misused or overdone, or when an individual is sick or disturbed at the start. In moderation, they afford the requisite control to handle the forces evoked. We live in an age of powerful machines and must arouse and direct intensified inner powers to cope with the pressures on every hand. Driving cars and flying in jet planes can be dangerous too, but most people don't hesitate to do these things. If, therefore, some breathing exercises can be mishandled, at least they are not as dangerous as not breathing at all. The Alternate Breathing exercise is probably the safest and most beneficial of those commonly practiced.

Even the psychic, or supernatural powers which yogis, shamans and magicians are said to induce through controlled respiration are "super" natural only in the sense of being *more* natural, as a supermarket is a bigger market or superessential is extremely essential. The breath is our great link with nature within and without, forever reminding us that we can not live unto ourselves alone. We may despise a certain person but still the air that was in him is now in us, and will be part of all that breathes for the rest of eternity.

In this way to be "super" natural means to clarify, intensify, interpret and glorify *nature.* We develop by penetrating to the heart of nature, rather than by going away from or beyond it.

This involves becoming more than ourselves, just as a plant is more than its seed, or an adult more than the child he was. Identity remains but with fuller expression. Deep breathing is the first and most direct way whereby we may increase our capacity to enter into the universal spirit of nature.

THE COMPLETE BREATH

Yogis sometimes call this exercise "The Bellows" because it is said to fan the flame of the mind with air, and make the body burn its fuel more efficiently. We will, however, call it the Complete Breath, to emphasize its integrative effect.

Sit quietly with spine erect and imagine as you inhale that you are being filled, just as the level of water would rise in a cup. Let the breath pour freely into the bottom, then the midsection, and finally to the top of your lungs. Be aware of each successive stage and at the end hold your breath about two seconds, as though replete to the very top. Then exhale through the nose and contract your stomach muscles firmly to make sure that all the air is squeezed out. Exhaling through your nose is better than using your mouth because it allows more control and prevents overstraining your lungs.

As you breathe in, energy should seem to flow right down your spine to its base. As your diaphragm lowers and your abdomen relaxes, the entire solar plexus area is stimulated. Next the midsection of your lungs fills, with your ribs pressing outward and your chest beginning to swell. Finally your upper chest rises slightly. There will be a sense of fullness in your throat right up to your forehead.

This is a powerful stimulant and generally should not be practiced more than a few times at a sitting. Seven repetitions are plenty for most people and it is better to begin with three to five. Dealing with these subtle forces of the breath can be like handling radiation. Effects are neither visible nor immediately felt, yet are powerful beyond belief. Just as X rays are produced by sending a current of electricity through a vacuum, so emptying the mind of its usual thought content and invoking dynamic currents of psychic energy, can induce a kind of spiritual radiance and clairvoyant faculties. The aim of the yogis who practiced it originally was to see through to the essence of things.

The Complete Breath serves not only as a nerve bath and lung cleanser, but intensifies responsiveness to the differing zones of the body and their psychological resonances. As you might pluck a violin string at different points to produce varying tones, or tune a radio to higher or lower wave lengths on its band, certain sensitive areas along your spine and in your head pick up and transmit vibrations of varying quality. These vortices of psychic energy are called "chakras," meaning wheels or centers, and like colors, or the notes of a scale, are said to be seven in number. We are discussing mainly the head, heart and solar plexus centers.

Just as the breath rises in the body, so can our unconscious forces (those centered below the diaphragm) be lifted first to the solar plexus, then to the region of the heart, and finally into the head by an act of will and visualization. There is evidence that this focusing of attention in the forehead affects the pituitary gland, which triggers off the rest of the glandular responses, and especially affects the body's ability to adapt to stress.

The interesting thing about stress is that the body does not know whether it is caused by physical or psychological factors. It doesn't respond to the *kind* but to the *degree* of stress. Either way it meets the challenge with the same systemic response. First, the pituitary gland sets off an alarm reaction which activates the adrenal glands and arouses the body's defenses. Second, an adaptation phase sets in and the organism learns how to cope with and adjust to the new demands. If the stress is too violent or prolonged a third stage ensues, characterized by exhaustion and breakdown.

In this manner, it is through the pituitary gland that mental states are translated into body chemistry. *Here mind and matter meet.* Students of yoga and meditation believe that the process can be reversed so that physiological forces can be transmuted into mental energies by being raised up the spine and concentrated in the forebrain area. Often they experience a sensation of illumination like a light in the head, which is the origin of the halo that artists depict above the heads of illumined persons.

Those interested in achieving a deeper understanding of the mechanism of stress and its psychological and philosophical implications should read Dr. Hans Selye's revolutionary book, *The Stress Of Life*. Dr. Selye discusses the results of a lifetime of painstaking medical research and makes it clear that in the final analysis it is not disease that kills us but stress. Stress is the basic cause of the many ailments which plague us, including obesity. If the body's general defense system is constantly being mobilized by mental tensions, resistance to the vicissitudes of cold, hunger and fatigue is decreased proportionately. Faith cures often work because when the organism is released from mental tensions, the system is freed to repair even the ravages of chronic diseases. Not only does the reserve become available for restoration and regeneration, but it allows for an extension of our mental influence into our surroundings.

An emotional explosion is just about the most expensive luxury your body can afford because of the requirements of its glandular response. In terms of energy a single pound of uranium can produce more heat than one thousand tons of coal, but the energy it takes to produce the uranium is equivalent to that of the thousand tons. Within the body the energy cost of creating hormones secreted by the glands is tremendous, compared with the relatively slight cost of producing glycogen which fuels your muscles and nerves. Therefore, undue stress is truly exhausting even if "only in the mind." The body can't tell the difference because it is included with the mind in a single unitary system of responses. As far as it knows thoughts are things.

We must remember, however, that stress is basically a positive incentive toward growth and development. The adrenaline and noradrenaline, which by overstimulating the system, can result in an oxygen deficit in the heart and contribute to a fatal attack, serve also as accelerators to speed up the heart action when the body needs energy to meet an emergency, and regulate the flow of blood through the body. The best corrupted becomes the worst, and so we are murdered by our own physical and psychological defenses. The act of smoking, for example, which is thought to be relaxing, actually aggravates and accelerates heart disease by overstimulating the sympathetic nervous system as would any other stress. Fear, anxiety, and fat are all such defenses which offend and perpetuate themselves through the conditions they are supposed to counter.

The solution is not to repress but to rechannel the stressful feelings that beset us. They should not be pushed down into the depths but must be brought up and let out. The following technique helps effect this liberation by raising and redirecting the vital forces of your body. This exercise will help you feel dynamic by taking a position of positive aspiration.

THE SUBLIMATING BREATH

To accomplish the Sublimating Breath stand with your feet apart and extend your arms as high as you can reach. Feel the force of gravity pressing the soles of your feet to the ground and pulling your body back to earth as it exerts a wearisome drag on each pound of flesh. Your body is composed mostly of water, and water tends to run downhill. Now make a second effort to raise yourself a little higher until your body is stretched to the utmost limit of its endurance. Breathe slowly and deliberately. Think of the ceaselessly burning fire of energy which moves through you like a flame pointing heavenward. The shape of a flame is not very different from that of a drop of water, yet they tend in opposite directions. Stretch still farther and identify with this up-force of life which impels trees and flowers and even the most delicate of earth's creatures to shoot up against the eternal pull of gravity. Feel the vigor pulsing through your fingertips, blending with the atmosphere and merging with space beyond. Let this rising power seem to do the pulling and stretching until you can stand no more. Realize that in asserting your will to stand in this position of confidence and determination you are filled with renewed strength.

At the end, lie supine and relaxed in the Floating position. Sense how the horizontal position subtly affects your entire psychology.

The Sublimating Breath counters the slow slide to senility with the aspiration to rise to new heights of accomplishment. Too often the heaviness of aging means not just the loss of youthful high spirits, but a bulging accumulation of fat on the lower parts of the body. Biologically the body reacts to the stress and insecurity of daily existence with a kind of cellular conservatism, as though the flesh itself were loath to part with its gains. As one renowned beauty remarked, "My figure is the same as it was twenty years ago — except that everything is lower than it used to be."

Happiness, as well as youth, is associated with upward tending movements. The corners of the mouth are raised in smiles, eyes light up, the heart leaps and one could jump for joy. Sorrow and aging alike are reflected in hunched shoulders, a down-at-the-mouth attitude, sinking heart and drooping demeanor.

It took all the ages of evolution for creatures to develop to the stage where they could crawl and raise themselves skyward. Only man can stand fully erect and lift his face toward the stars; yet he hardly sees them. Too many people slowly return to the stance of the ape simply because they don't take measures to remain straight by reaching for higher things.

During the span of a human life the body unfolds like a flower, from the fetal position, through crawling stages, until the youth glories in his capacity to stand alone, straight and tall, able to maintain himself as a self-sufficient human being. By middle age many people have already started to revert to the fetal position. Their bodies curve in like flower petals beginning to shrivel until finally they hunch over into old age. First they grow up, then they grow down. The decline can, however, be reversed if you will practice standing upright with arms stretched high, head back and your chest expanded to receive the breath of life.

3

Breathing, Relaxation and Autosuggestion

YOUR BREATH FOLLOWS A HIGHWAY leading straight into the unconscious. At one end it is voluntary and controlled by your mind. At the other it is involuntary and controlled by your nerves. Above all, it is a *way* by which you can communicate between conscious and unconscious realms of your being, and a way along which two-directional traffic can travel.

We are concerned with reshaping the body, and since it is the unconscious mind which rules the physiological functions, it behooves us to exploit any possible means for remaining on good terms with this unseen but ever present partner. In relating to the self, as in all social relations, knowledge brings understanding, cooperation and mutual concern.

To speak to the body or unconscious mind requires techniques rather different from those used in conversing with other people, although the same courteous consideration and respect must prevail. If you are just trying to jam the "lid on the id" or flaunt your superiority to a mass, or mess, of surly instincts, then the effort is not worth making. In this respect the word *un*conscious means something different from *sub*conscious. The prefix "sub," meaning lower, can misguide, since this extension of our consciousness is not only broader at its base than the isolated pinnacle of our self-awareness, but connects all the way around with ranges of experience that can be called super-conscious. Whenever possible, therefore, we prefer to use the word "psyche" with its intimations of the beautiful Greek goddess of the soul.

To train the instincts governing the body demands an approach similar to one you might use in dealing with a small child. The child may be innately sweet but you still don't like him to shriek, break things, or soil his pants, and it is contingent on you to make your position clear. This may prove difficult if the child has been spoiled, for then you may be compelled to override violent protests until he learns to behave. At the same time you must not forget that he is a potential man, even when acting like a little beast.

Your instincts, though vastly energetic, are still preliterate and you must use a special language of repetition and pictures in dealing with them, remembering that they are motivated by pleasure, pain and reward, not by ethics or morality. They couldn't care less for abstract reasoning and excessive verbalization. It has been said that when will and imagination collide, imagination always triumphs. It is the power to visualize which opens up channels through which forces of will and desire flow into action. Whether a suggestion is positive or negative is not as relevant as the clarity of the image. If someone shouts, "Don't look!" immediately eyes swing in the forbidden direction. Tell yourself, "Don't eat," and back comes a resounding echo of "EAT, EAT, eat." The abstract "do not" is dropped but the image of eating remains and multiplies like reflections in ruffled water.

The rules of autosuggestion are *visualization* and *repetition*. Breathing adds force to both. The influence of repetition is evidenced by our responses to liturgical ritual, chanting, hand clapping, political slogans, exhortations of cheerleaders, beating of drums, rock and roll music, and songs with many choruses, as well as our sentimental attachments to familiar people, places and ideas. Advertisers take full advantage of the hypnotic effects of repetition and the childish propensity to be lulled by the same story told in the same words. In this way they actually induce us to behave like children. Repetition, like the blows of a hammer pounding a nail, causes penetration and fixation of the idea stressed.

The most basic, repetitious phenomenon we know is breathing. The singing, chanting, huckstering and storytelling to which we have just referred, is carried to us by sounds on the breath, moving us to the depths of our being. The thrill of our answering responses seems to come from the body itself, which, like a tuning fork, vibrates sympathetically to ideas translated into its wave length.

Words are magic, but only when there is some inspiration behind them weaving a potent spell. In many scriptures the act of creation is described as a divine word, command, syllable or song. Now, scientists present data to demonstrate that varying pulsations account for the appearance and organization of all matter. Substance reduces to electrical vibrations, positive, negative, or neutral, keyed to differing frequencies in a manner reminiscent of the Pythagorean concept of the music of the spheres. All that seems to us so palpably solid can be analyzed into ever finer particles, until we are left with the intangible energies of sound, light and motion. Or as a scientist put it, "We know too much about matter to be materialists."

Hindu philosophers used to say that evolution is divided into three stages, each one having its appropriate yoga or way to self-realization. These are the epochs of the Yantra, the Mantra, and the Tantra. Yantra are mystical diagrams, the modern-day equivalent being a blueprint of a machine or electrical circuit. Mantra are spells or words of power. The Tantra is a system for producing a resolution of opposites. At this time we are emerging from the age of the machine, or Yantra, to enter an era when men will become more sensitive to words and subtle vibrations. Existence will be seen not so much as a primordial machine or clock, wound up to tick on through eternity, but as a congeries of responsive lives resonating to one another. Only at the end does the age of the Tantra bring about a resolution of Spirit and Matter, God and Nature, as a result of this cosmic intercourse.

Our individual development can be divided into the same three stages. As long as we regard the body as a kind of machine, there is little we can do except attend to its parts and hope it functions. It eats to grow hungry again, produces babies to produce more babies, and so on, with mechanical regularity. No real changes are made, or sought. In fact the body positively resists change, and so evolves slowly and only adapts to forces coming from the external environment.

When your body is considered not as a robot but as a dynamic system of organized processes, not as your only self but as a vital extension of your inner being, then you can talk to it as to a living entity, and evoke an answering response. In other words, there is the possibility of change and regeneration from within. Conflict arises because of this experienced duality, but so does the potential for creativity and growth.

Only in the individuated personality does there occur that re-integration, which is the goal of yoga, whereby the higher self recalls its image and the two are united. Man is said to be ape and angel conjoined. But often he can not attain the higher state because he fails to admit the animal below. You can not jump up without first crouching down, but the crouching is also part of the jumping. Every union is really a re-union of that which has been separated in the play of the universe with its own true self and origin.

The principle of advance through retreat (a variation of the law of reverse effort) holds that we can not reach the superconscious directly from the ego, but must go through the subconscious. That is why the intellectualism of modern academic disciplines will never save the world, nor enable us to save ourselves. Science has not prevented us from going to war. If anything, over-emphasizing the development of the mind leads to outbreaks of repressed, irrational and violent tendencies, as occurred in Hitler's Germany. No country has ever had better educational facilities than present-day America, yet the nation as a whole seems obsessed with intrigue and violence, confined not just to movies and television, but erupting in increasing crime.

The fact that we find divinity reflected in Nature and not in the machinations of the rational mind is significantly portrayed in the symbolism of the Tarot cards of the medieval Cabalists. On the face of the card called the Lovers is a man (representing the ego or conscious self), a woman (representing the unconscious or earthy instinctual self) and an angel (representing the divine self). The man is looking down at the woman, who in turn looks up at the angel whose enfolding wings encompass both together in harmonious symmetry.

Much is written these days about the power of positive thinking, and almost everyone tries to practice it to some extent, even if for negative reasons. It usually involves making suggestions to yourself about improving attitude, drive, and determination to succeed. Few stop to realize, however, that talking to yourself works better, if you have some idea to whom you are talking, and if you know the language. Autosuggestion has its own formalized etiquette as specific as the rules and conventions which exist in any polite society. Merely to affirm, "Every day in every way I am shrinking thinner and thinner," will have about the same effect as sending a letter to a dictator saying that you don't like his policy in running his country and think he should change it. What is needed is popular support. Fortunately democratic processes do exist and there are ways of getting the message through, at least in an enlightened society. If enough of the population can be brought into agreement, or if even a few can become sufficiently articulate, these feelings can be registered and put into action.

The means to make your will effective in relation to your body are: (1) Integration (2) Concentration (3) Right technique. Breathing can provide the motive power for all three.

1. Integration.

Diaphragmatic Breathing serves to align the subtle forces of your body just as stroking an iron bar with a magnet re-orders its molecules and renders them capable of attracting particles of a similar nature. This may not produce visible results, any more than a magnet appears different from other pieces of iron, but an entirely new purpose may be served because of the inner alteration.

Singers, orators and people in show business who must study and master breathing in order to project their voices and hold an audience, often develop vivacious, magnetic and attractive personalities. They can step up on a stage and "belt" out a song or speech because literally the power rises from the belt-line traveling up the conduit of the spine, from solar plexus to head, bringing the whole body into dynamic synthesis.

Two actors may look the same at first view, but while one goes through his well-studied motions, the other scintillates with an enthusiasm that galvanizes all who watch. The difference is between a personality at odds with itself, like a pipe-line with the joints askew, and one integrated to constitute a direct channel for power of an intensity which raises the performance to greatness. The result is not just technically superior but takes on a new dimension of expressiveness.

The goal of most people's endeavors is to be well adjusted, normal, successful citizens. Yet there are always the few for whom this is not enough, who find themselves dissatisfied with the usual satisfactions and must turn their steps to the path of higher evolution. They are the ones who are beginning to radiate that peculiarly luminous quality which we call "soul power," and their impact upon the world is far more potent than their everyday actions seem to justify.

Only when all components of a personality or production smoothly intermesh with regard to a central purpose, are we inspired by this sense of completion that, in rejecting no part, redeems all, transcending their sum to become a new whole, wholesome, or even holy. Those who can exert all their faculties for the sake of a worthy cause can become integrated, being diminished only where they fail to give.

The seriously overweight person is not an integrated being. He has tended to reject some vital instinct or some part of his anatomy, usually associated with the area below the waist. At the very least he has given up the desire to look his best. Psychological tests conducted by motivational researchers have proven that the obese person fails to identify with his body or to see himself as others see him. As much as possible, he tunes the fact of being fat right out of his consciousness. Intelligence seems to have little to do with it, since some people compensate for physical deficiencies by exercising their mind. They deny that their superior reasoning power involves any responsibility for developing a similarly superior body.

Even when preoccupied with their condition, overweight people still tend to be unrealistic in blaming their heaviness for problems which really are the cause and not the effect of fat. An inadequate love life, for example, may be not as much a result of obesity, as of the fear of sex. Being engrossed with superficial deficiencies of figure, rather than with figuring out what character traits have produced these deficiencies, they are particularly prone to snap at any diet that promises easy help no matter how faddish. If the diet is sufficiently spectacular, it can distract from the unglamorous issues of *why* it was necessary to overeat at all.

Many overweight people can't bear to look at themselves from the waist down. They hate their bulging stomach, as though it were no part of themselves. They will pay fantastic prices for reducing devices to express this anger (or relieve frustration) by thumping, squeezing, shaking, melting, or pounding away at the hapless flesh. Buying corsets and expensive exercise equipment may purchase a temporary illusion of decrease (in the pocketbook it can be justifiably real) but if they refuse to confront the true problem, assuaging their guilt by spending money instead, then thwarted nature fights back with all the fury of a woman scorned.

The unrealistic attitudes associated with the problems of being overweight are evident in the superficial treatment of dieting in most magazines and books. Philosophers overlook the subject and sociologists and psychologists have produced few theories or methods for inspiring people to keep in shape. The church has bypassed the issue from both moral and practical points of view. Yet the matter is not silly or irrelevant to those living in perpetual physical and mental discomfort, or to the millions whose lives are cut short by diseases aggravated by obesity. To many people committing suicide with a gun shows bad form, but suicide with cigarettes, alcohol and gluttonous eating signifies normal good taste.

For thousands of years mankind has had to fight nature to establish a toehold on this seemingly inhospitable planet. Not until a fairly high degree of civilization is attained do we find poets and artists extolling the charms of living creatures and lovely places. Little by little, the desire to ravage the earth for its food and goods is superceded by a more enlightened appreciation of the goodness of nature and an effort to beautify parks, protect animals, and enhance cities with grass and trees. Similarly the truly civilized man finally realizes that his human nature is not something to mow down and pave over, but to cultivate and esteem. Self-integration requires a philosophy that allows us to accept and value ourselves esthetically as well as pragmatically. Our concern for making the body a fitting habitation for the soul reflects our profoundest philosophy and the extent of our reverence for life.

2. Concentration.

The intimate association of breathing and mental concentration was discussed in our last chapter. It is not just your mind which must be sharpened and made one-pointed, but the whole driving force of your personality. Since energy follows thought, you can channel your will-to-accomplishment into action by creative visualization. The following exercises of the imagination are examples of ways in which your higher aspirations can be grounded in the physiological reality of breathing to enable you to focus and direct your intent.

VITALIZING VISUALIZATION

A. Breathe in deeply while extending your right arm in front of you as far as it will reach. Imagine your arm as a pipeline through which force flows, emerging directly from your heart. Feel the power streaming into your fingers until they seem to tingle. Hold this position while you continue to visualize these subtle radiations pouring out through your fingertips into space. Then, while exhaling, slowly bring your fingers back to your heart and try to sense the vital force returning to the center of your body. Repeat, using your left arm.

B. Lying flat on your back, raise and lower your legs with knees straight, alternating to the rhythm of your breathing. Inhale as a leg is raised and exhale as it is lowered. Imagine that each leg is a rod which you are magnetizing with your breath while the life force from your heart flows through them, just as it did through your arms.

C. Place your hands on your solar plexus and inhale deeply several times, as though breathing through your abdomen. Sense your physical body being flooded with vitalizing power, revivifying all cells and tissues.

D. Rest your hands on your heart. In like manner imagine that you are drawing in the current of life from the midpoint of your chest and that this is expanding your emotional capacity to appreciate, respond and love. Feel that you, as prime motivator, relate to your body just as the heart in the chest circulates oxygen-laden blood to each organ and limb. Be aware of the floor, the room, the earth as a whole, and of the many lines of connection which your imagination projects like rays from the center of yourself out into people, places, and things.

E. Hold your hands to your forehead, palms over eyes, fingers up, and practice breathing as though from behind your eyes. Imagine a golden light streaming through them and soothing the tissues of your brain. Allow this gentle luminosity to permeate your mind with healing peace.

F. Finally, just meditate on the act of breathing, the rhythmic sensation of motion and expansion. Consider how the breath, an intangible essence that can be neither seen nor grasped, gives rise to our capacity to experience the dazzling realm of the senses. Do not make a deliberate effort to expand your chest but allow the breath to do the moving. Try to think, not that you are a body which contains life, but that you *are* that larger Life itself seeking expression through multitudes of bodies, of which yours is only one. *Be* that overflowing Power flooding through the evanescent forms of existence shining from within.

Concentration on the breath as motive power and inspiration does not just improve one's "self-image" in the sense currently in vogue, which suggests the flickering unreality of a picture projected on a movie screen. Rather it is an endeavor to reflect the true Self, the essential identity behind the shifting shadow-play of our desires. We seek not only to be illumined, but to identify with the source of illumination.

To con-centrate, literally to bring to a central point, gives point to our lives. When the fragments of our personality begin to cohere, all existence seems more coherent. We develop the senses in order to make sense of the world. Signs become significant, means determine meanings, and to inhale is to be inspired, the birthright of all.

3. Technique.

If you are ill and need a certain serum, it does little good to rub it on the skin. Better to put it in a hypodermic and thrust the needle directly into the body. Positive thinking must also be concentrated and then injected deep into the unconscious mind to take proper effect. In this respect we can learn from the hypnotist who knows that the more he can persuade his subjects to relax, the more potent his influence will be, and the deeper his suggestions will penetrate. Relaxation removes the barriers between the conscious and unconscious states, as in sleep and hypnosis.

Autosuggestion concerning diet, smoking, temper, or whatever it may be that you wish to talk to yourself about, can be practiced most effectively when you are in a quiet, relaxed state of mind. The problem is how to achieve this receptive attitude. The average person can not relax just by wishing or willing it so, but he can induce repose by practicing the intense nonstrenuous kinds of physical exercises outlined in the exercise section of this book. Extreme exertion causes the glandular and nervous systems to act like a pendulum swinging toward the positive or active state. Automatically it will react in the opposite direction and swing back into a negative or passive state of relaxation, as soon as the body rests.

This is one reason why Shakers shake, Dervishes whirl, Yogis practice their asanas, Shamans dance, Hindus chant and Muslims bow down while praying. The more fervid the preparatory gyrations, the closer the resulting meditative condition is to a trance-like state, and the more the subconscious feelings are likely to break through in the form of visions and revelations. Churchgoers who sing hymns lustily, and then settle back to listen passively to the sermon, are likely to be in an intensely impressionable state of mind. The same is true of members of evangelistic sects. By the time a leader asks them if they are ready to be saved, much preparatory work has already been done through rhythm and repetition of key phrases.

In times of exertion, the sympathetic nervous system is activated by adrenaline, secreted by the glands and supplemented by adrenaline-like compounds given off by the nerves themselves. It is inherent in the balance of the body's economy that what the sympathetic nervous system does, the parasympathetic undoes, acting on the effector cells of muscles and glands by liberating acetylcholine, a substance which the nerves require to complete their synapses. The active state is called adrenergia, the passive state cholinergia.

Experiments described by Dr. Andrija Puharich in his remarkable book *Beyond Telepathy* seem to prove that in telepathic thought transference the adrenergic state favors sending and the cholinergic favors receiving. Since telepathy is mainly a function of the unconscious mind, it is not controlled by the brain as much as by the solar plexus and the complementary branches of the autonomic nervous system, the sympathetic and the para-sympathetic. Puharich reached the conclusion that in carrying out their rituals yogis are able to release at will the chemicals their bodies need to induce the required state of psychic receptivity.

Our systems are capable of manufacturing their own tran-quilizers, pep pills, and just about any antibody needed to fight off invading germs. The body can serve itself not only as physi-cian but as pharmacist. It can both diagnose and treat, given the conditions to carry on its work without interference.

All exercise sessions should end, therefore, with a period of deep relaxation and autoconditioning, allowing time to assimi-late what has been experienced. The body's chemical factory must compensate for the release of adrenaline (from the muscles) and noradrenaline (from the nerve endings) into the blood stream by restoring the oxygen balance through rest and deep breathing. In this way the nervous system regulators are trained to cope with sudden oxygen demands and the likeli-hood of a heart attack is considerably diminished. Heart injur-ies are caused by *oxygen* deficits resulting from stress, smoking, overweight and high-cholesterol diets, and not by strenuous activity. Exercise preserves the regulatory mechanisms which prevent the drain of oxygen.

Ordinary daily labor does not produce the same chemical reactions, or the same psychic receptivity as the systematic exer-cises of yoga. Body and mind are activated like two positive battery poles, or else both grow weary simultaneously, like two negatives. Either way no current flows. But when your mind is stimulated by the circulation of oxygen-laden blood to the brain cells, and at the same time your body is induced to relax, then energy is free to flow between positive mental and nega-tive physical poles, and a dialogue can be carried on with your deeper psyche.

It is of utmost importance that you do not just issue com-mands to the unconscious in the arrogant conviction that you, as ego, know what is best for its welfare. Learn to register images and inspirations from below. There exists, in this psychic realm, not only a vast storehouse of memories and desires, but also the guiding, directional principles which motivate all our conduct. Some people fear the idea of hypnosis, even the thought of hypnotizing themselves. They are correct in their assumption that you can't just go barging about in somebody's unconscious mind, not even your own, but they forget that we are all daily hypnotized by advertising, propaganda and the blandishments of the world. What we must do is *dehypnotize* ourselves to see things in their true perspective. If we work in cooperation with the psyche, heeding its wise promptings, a protection is afforded that the ego can never give.

The weight-weary dieter should study techniques of aligning conscious and unconscious sides of his personality, in order to effect a reconciliation of the mind that controls the body with the mind that controls its thinking. His good resolutions must be not just wishes or intentions to succeed, but a literal resolution of the opposition between instinct and intellect. The obese person's problem is so fundamental it can hardly be seen for its immediacy. Despite brooding over his inadequacies, he is still out of touch with himself. This lack of direct contact is reflected in an utter lack of comprehension of how little food or pampering the body requires. He isn't even aware of his own unawareness. He can not be *sensible* about himself until he is first *sensitive* to himself.

HEALING VISUALIZATION

We recommend that the following visualization exercise be practiced during relaxation and whenever you are in need of an instant uplift or a faith talk.

Lie down flat on your back and breathe Diaphragmatically. On each inhalation fill your mind with the idea, "I am breathing in the light, strength and confidence my body needs." Exhaling think, "I am breathing out anxiety, fatigue, all weariness and cares." Give substance to this thought by concentrating on the image of your body being swept clean by healing light during the inbreath, while on the outbreath picture all poisons, toxins, and fears melting away.

When you are habituated to this attitude of regarding your body as a pulsing web of light, your breathing rhythm provides the basis for a conditioned reflex. *Every* inhalation will serve as a reminder that you are drawing energy out of the great reservoir of universal power, and *every* exhalation will eliminate negative feelings and conditions. This process will continue unconsciously, regardless of where your conscious mind may be occupied. Each breath becomes like a bead in a rosary, a link joining others in a connecting chain that starts in your mind and head, reaches down into the depths of your body and psyche, and returns upon itself to complete the circuit and recharge your whole personality.

PART FOUR

The Yoga of Sex

1

Sex and Regeneration

SEX HAS GENERATIVE AND REGENERATIVE ASPECTS, depending on whether it is channeled through lower or higher avenues of expression. Had this instinct been implanted merely to insure reproduction it could have been limited to a brief flowering. A few well-timed acts of intercourse would have sufficed. But sex in human experience is not as much flowers or fruit (which drop from the tree) as the living sap in every limb. This vital urge diffuses through our activities just as hormones produced by the sex glands account for every change in physical appearance from infancy to old age. As fundamental as man's desire to give birth to children, is his desire to be reborn from day to day as a new and evolving entity. Self-duplication is but the evident physical aspect of a reality which, in its spiritual aspect, we call self-development. Both together move the world to progress.

In church-dominated countries it has long been the custom to decree that sex should be primarily confined to reproduction. (At present we are in the midst of a swing away from this point of view.) The emphasis has been on visible material results rather than on expansion of consciousness. The paradox in this attitude is that most religions have chosen to glorify the function of sex that man shares with the animals, while denying the validity of that function associated with love, which is the attribute of God.

A school of yoga known as the Tantra has for centuries been concerned with the science of regeneration through sex. Its disciples endeavor to arouse the forces locked in the lower centers and deliberately raise them to higher centers. These energies can be most intensely experienced, and thus made available for conscious direction, during sexual excitation or intercourse. The effect can be that of having an orgasm in the head with a great flash of light behind the eyes and tremendous stimulation of all higher mental and spiritual faculties. The entire system receives a tremendous charge as the libidinal forces are channeled up the spine and conserved, instead of being discharged below.

Sometimes this is taken literally to mean that no semen is released, and that the fluid is retained in the body to be transmuted into a spiritual potency known as "ojas" which promotes remarkable psychic abilities, including longevity. This interpretation has given rise to a widespread fear that normal intercourse would result in a loss of power and deplete the system. Consequently many Hindus are more puritanical than Christians in regarding women as objects of peril and temptation. But considerable research has failed to prove that sex in any way drains the body of strength. Physiological studies have found it excellent for the heart and circulation, a fact most lovers have always suspected.

The progressive disciplines of yoga involve quieting the body, holding the breath, restraining the senses and stilling the mind, in order to distinguish between the knower and that which is known. The yogi, in suspending outward motion, accomplishes the same result as the scientist who strictly controls his variables in order to discover a causal factor. The difference is that in yoga the observer includes himself in the experiment, whereas the scientist endeavors to remain detached from that which he observes. The yogi observes even his own detachment.

The same restraint applies in the yoga of sex. The partners may merely contemplate one another, or endeavor to immobilize their bodies to achieve heightened awareness of and control over the forces aroused. In India and Tibet there are many temples decorated with carvings or pictures depicting deities clasped in carnal embrace of such variety that one can only stand awed at this spectacle of "divine" ingenuity. Most Tantric scholars insist that it is all symbolic, and that these images are strictly for meditation. When men and women seek to emulate them they don't practice such poses for the sake of novelty or titillation, but for spiritual advancement through the discipline of fixity.

Sacramental sex is abysmally misunderstood in both East and West. The link between sex and regeneration has been especially twisted in the Occident because it is alien to our temperament to associate human desire with worship of the cosmic energy latent in every individual, or to see anything but primitive lasciviousness in phallic symbolism. Yet Webster's *Dictionary* defines the word "sacral" as "of or for religious rites," and also as "pertaining to, or in the region of, the sacrum." The words "devil" and "divine" derive from the same Sanskrit root meaning "shining," and Lucifer is the "bearer of light."

The connection is far more explicit in innumerable Hindu temples and roadside shrines containing the Siva lingam which devotees deck with flowers and the pious lave with oil and ghee. One of the most renowned of all such holy places is the sacred cave of Amarnath, reached only by a perilous three-day trek across Himalayan glaciers, to which the faithful flock from every part of the land to witness the miracle of the great ice lingam which mysteriously waxes and wanes in size with the phases of the moon. Every deity has his consort, in contrast to Christianity, which allows a Father and a Son, but overlooks the Mother for the sake of something called a Holy Ghost!

To the Hindu the lingam signifies not the male organ as much as the sublime procreative power of the universe. That which is symbolized originated with God, the Creator, not with man, His image. But as Voltaire pointed out, God created man in His image and man returned the compliment. Those imbued with the psychology of the West tend to associate all phallic symbols with their mortal counterparts. Anything smacking of sex magic becomes a prurient mystery. Evidently they assume that using sex as a force for higher development is worse than confining it to gratification of the senses and bringing children into an overpopulated world.

The belief that sex should exist as much for pleasure as for procreation is expressed by the Hindu conception that the cosmos itself is not just God's offspring — a thing set apart from Himself — but that it is an eternal love-play or "lila" carried on between male and female aspects of divinity (Purusha and Prakriti). All existence is the act of God, the Father, loving Mother Nature, and in their exuberance showering forth stars and sparkling worlds of light. In every sense God *is* Love! Because this unitive impulse lies at the origin of each particle of creation the universe itself is engaged in a cosmic yoga of synthesis. All that man does, God did first.

The charge has frequently been made that yoga exercises, especially those involving breath control, are sexually stimulating. We can not deny this implication, since if the whole organism is energized all its functions are intensified. The practice of yoga can be like fertilizing a garden. It helps produce beautiful flowers and also a host of weeds. (Even the higher stages of concentration and meditation can produce ego inflation.) If the cultivator is not diligent and discriminating the weeds may overwhelm the flowers. Properly channeled sexual appetite is an efflorescence of health and joy, so that anything which makes you more vital is also likely to make you sexier.

Yoga teaches that the sexually mature individual should endeavor to blend his highest capacity for love with his fundamental instincts to achieve at-one-ment. It is not better techniques that are required as much as a release of the mediating power of the self, in order to heal the cleavage between flesh and spirit that has crucified humanity for eons. The secret of being a good lover lies not in making love, but in loving.

A wholesome diet, exercise, deep breathing and meditation all serve to enhance awareness of the magnetic quality that causes you to be physically and sexually attractive. According to the theory of yoga the basic impulses of sex flow up and down the spine, taking various forms of expression according to the level they have reached. Yet they rise from one root source at the base of the vertebral column. Sex is considered to be not just the physical structure that makes us masculine or feminine, but the driving force energizing the entire personality.

The anatomical composition of the body symbolizes these differing levels of consciousness which make up your psychic mechanism. The physical nature is represented by the area from the diaphragm down. (Traditionally the diaphragm was considered to be the "horizon" dividing conscious and unconscious zones of the body.) This lower part is given over to housing the digestive and reproductive organs concerned with material survival. Here, too, are the adrenal glands impelling you to act and assert yourself, and your main heating, plumbing and storage areas, somewhat analogous to the basement of a house. The legs, like twin tap roots, through which run the sciatic nerve (largest of all nerves) and the most massive bones, connect you solidly with the earth. The solar plexus, sometimes termed the "animal brain" or "psychic storage battery," serves as the central clearing house controlling the autonomic nervous system and unconscious economy of your body.

The area from your waist up to your neck represents your emotional or feeling nature. This is the zone which connects your higher and lower parts, and contains the circulatory and respiratory systems which join your body as a whole. Metaphorically we assign to the heart the urge to unify and relate called love, but literally, too, it is the pivotal point from which every artery emanates and toward which every vein returns. As the earth is tipped toward the sun at an angle of twenty-three and one-half degrees (the obliquity of the ecliptic) so is the heart tipped at the same angle to the body. Emotions are registered mainly in this mediating area since it is your sympathies and antipathies which cause you to feel related to your environment. Negative conditions may be registered as a sinking sensation in the stomach, a lump in the throat or a pain in the neck. On the positive side, the heart can swell with joy and the chest expand with pride. Sinking and shrinking sensations are painful while rising and expanding sensations betoken joy.

The area from the neck up represents your mental life and voluntary actions. Here are the control centers for the senses, motor functions and general intelligence. At this north or upper pole the mouth draws in sustenance that, in turn is eliminated at the lower pole. What people think about things is reflected mainly in facial expressions. We furrow the forehead, raise the eyebrows, blink, wink, wrinkle the nose, smile, sneer, gape, pout, twitch or jut out the chin. These movements are more likely to show conscious responses to messages brought in to the brain by the senses, than are the lower unconscious reactions. The eyes, forebrain and pituitary gland represent the highest command center while the heart dominates the chest region and the solar plexus the pelvic region.

You can often tell where a person's attention is focused by the direction in which the hands wander. Hands serve as go-betweens for the three sectors, but are especially indicative of feelings. The drinking man in a saloon tends to slap his thigh as he recounts an off-color story. The distraught mother beats her breast and wrings her hands while her spouse clenches his fists. The scholar rubs his forehead or pulls his hair.

Even arms and legs carry out the threefold plan of creation. The upper parts of the arms and legs give physical power, since they stem directly from the trunk. The midsection is adaptive and the hands are deliberately expressive, with five fingers to represent the five senses, of which one is paramount. Like the senses, hands and feet connect us with the world, whether to reshape it or walk upon it.

To pursue this concept further, you can think of the front side of the torso as soft, passive, relaxed and feminine, while the back expresses the stiff, hard, assertive male principle. Thus the stomach wants to droop to earth, but the strong backbone and back muscles keep the body pointed heavenward.

Your spinal column is the connecting link between the three zones of the body, and this is one reason why exercises to strengthen and align the segments of your back produce such an integrative effect upon your whole personality. From mid-back down, the spinal cord branches out in a myriad of rootlike fibers. Above are pairs of nerves extending from the cord, like tiered petals. Finally, from the medulla oblongata to the cerebrum, twelve large cranial nerves, like a calyx, support the brain, the flower of biological evolution.

While your hands travel outwardly to all parts of the body, and the stalk of the spine innervates its complex organic structure, the central unifying factor and symbol of universal life is the breath which animates the body as a whole, and whose absence leaves but a decaying corpse. Correctly practiced yogic breathing exercises serve to relate the positive pole in the head to the negative pole at the coccyx, through conscious control and direction of the vital forces. The physical positions mainly insure that the conduit be straight and clear. If they seem to be sexually stimulating this occurs less because of direct pressure upon the lower areas than because of the cleansing of the channels through which the entire body is invigorated. Sex is "dirty" only when these energies are blocked, perverted or allowed to stagnate uselessly, just as water which flows nowhere becomes fetid. Healthy sex is also clean because physically and psychologically both partners feel open and free to express all elements of their nature in harmonious interaction.

Some people aspiring toward self-development seem to believe that the way to open up higher channels is to block off the lower. Unless this repudiation of normal desire happens naturally because of age or innate disinclination for sexual relationships, it seldom leads to any particularly constructive results. We must, however, consider that certain types of people, such as monks and nuns, may have a special vocation in undertaking the discipline of celibacy.

For most people, fighting the body in order to engage in excessive prayer and meditation is like trying to pry apart the petals of a bud to make it bloom. If the aspirant will engage in the apparently unglamorous work of tending the roots, the flower will gladly blossom of its own accord. Anyone can weed, water and scratch about in the dirt at the base of a plant, but only nature can make it unfold to the sun and air. If, therefore, we will minister to our bodies, wherein lie the instinctual roots of personality, our lives will flower and bring forth fruit, all in their own good time.

2

Sex, The Sacred Fire

SEX, LIKE ELECTRICITY, is an inherently mysterious phenomenon. We exist because of it, can experience or even be "shocked" by it. Still it remains an intangible presence.

Like light, sex is known by that which it reveals, yet behind the surface glitter and shadow play of desires lies the unfathomed darkness of the unseen source. We call these forces of creation electricity or we call them sex, according to our point of view. As the gap between living and nonliving matter shrinks under the scrutiny of electron microscopes, and as a result of the success of chemists in synthesizing organic compounds, it appears increasingly probable that the responsive principle which in inanimate objects we know as electricity, in animate creatures takes on the guise of sex.

This fundamental magnetism of the body which Western psychologists refer to as libido has long been known to yogis as "Kundalini," the "serpent power" or "sacred fire." Kundalini is considered to be a goddess because "she" lies coiled at the negative or feminine pole of the spine and energizes the material aspect of creation. During the course of individual self-development Kundalini is said to unfold and mount upward in serpentine convolutions through the seven centers of the body. Each of these centers, called a lotus or "chakra," corresponds to a nerve plexus and to a gland. Their function is to galvanize the body into action, just as the glands do, but they were known and described by yogis many hundreds of years before anything was known about the operations of the human glandular system.

The chakras are vortices of psychic energy which to the clairvoyant view seem to spin like wheels. (Chakra means wheel in Sanskrit.) They are also called lotuses because of the characteristic petal-like form of the rays they emanate, which varies from one center to another.

Their correspondences are as follows:

PHYSICAL LOCATION	SANSKRIT NAME	CORRESPONDING GLAND	NUMBER OF PETALS
1. Base of Spine	Muladhara	Adrenals	4
2. Lumbar Region	Swadhisthana	Sex Glands	6
3. Solar Plexus	Manipura	Pancreas	10
4. Heart	Anahata	Thymus	12
5. Throat	Vishuda	Thyroid	16
6. Brow	Ajna	Pituitary	96 (2)*
7. Cerebrum	Brahmaranda	Pineal	1000

*The 96 petals of the brow chakra are divided into two winglike formations.

The science of the interplay of subtle or pranic forces throughout major and minor centers and their resultant effects upon the body is exceedingly recondite and has in the past been considered so secret that its existence has been veiled from the public. Sometimes the centers are divided into three below the diaphragm and three above, coordinated by the seventh or brow center. Those below reflect those above so that energy can be transmuted along three main lines extending: (1) from the solar plexus to the heart, (2) from the sex center to the throat, and finally (3) from the base of the spine to the top of the head. The pituitary is the master control for the entire body.

The throat center is associated with creativity and hence the connection between sex organs (which it polarizes) and the timbre of the voice as well as the thyroid gland. Divine creation is said to be the outcome of a Word, Logos, or series of uttered vibrations. Artists tend to have unusual sex lives because they are endeavoring to manipulate forces oscillating between reproductive and productive chakras. Because of the inner linkage, exercise students sometimes find that the Shoulderstand (with its pressure on the neck and thyroid gland) stimulates their sex life.

As each center is vivified corresponding levels of consciousness open out and higher powers of body and mind are attained. The spine becomes like an iron bar magnetized by being wound round with electrified wire, causing the whole body to radiate. By deep breathing, concentration and meditation upon the raising of these pranic forces through the centers along the spine and into the head, the practitioner of yoga can elect to produce, by a brief intensive effort, the same results that would eventually come to pass in the evolutionary scheme of existence. There is nothing strange or unnatural in this hastening of normal progress. It only accelerates the pace.

The dangers in Kundalini yoga stem from the fact that one is literally playing with fire, and fire burns. Unless the individual's motives are pure, and his body and mind likewise purified by long continued discipline, he should not experiment with the electricity of the body. Even an advanced student of yoga working under the supervision of a teacher risks a certain amount of nervous strain and overstimulation. A person who follows the regular path of evolution is like a traveler wending his way along a mountain trail, ascending by barely perceptible stages. If, in his desire to reach the top sooner, he turns his steps and beats his way upward, blazing his own course, not only does the journey become more difficult, but he quickly reaches hazardous heights where a fall, that would previously have been negligible, can mean disaster.

The concept of serpent power appears in the snake symbolism which runs through many of the myths of the world. The hero must conquer a dragon, sea monster, or some obviously snakelike antagonist in order to release an imprisoned or sleeping princess. Hercules strangled a pair of snakes in the cradle. The inhabitants of the Garden of Eden, cradle of Western culture, were not so fortunate. They did not succeed in expelling the snake from the Garden, but since a conflict had begun that was bound to end with the expulsion of *something,* they themselves were driven out. Forever after sex has been considered the root of sin and shame. Adam and Eve took with them the serpent of greed and self-gratification, leaving behind the good snake entwined among the branches of the Tree of Life. In Oriental cultures the serpent often stands for power and wisdom. The snake with his tail in his mouth has long been the symbol of eternity. Whether the serpent is considered evil or wise, a dealer of death or eternal life, depends largely upon the prevailing attitude toward sex of the culture in which the myth is embedded.

A positive example of the serpent symbolism is the caduceus carried by Mercury, messenger of the gods, with its twin snakes coiling up the staff, ending in a pair of wings representing spiritual liberation. (The wings also represent the brow chakra.) The belief that the secret of health is found in man's ability to be conjoined within himself is preserved in the caduceus, emblem of the medical profession. To achieve wholesomeness man must be able to commune with various levels of his consciousness. Hence Mercury stands for communications and the telephone company whose wires serve as nerves in the body of society. We find the symbolism of the staff in the king's scepter, the magician's wand, the staff of Moses, and the rod of power wielded by the priests of certain religious sects.

The prana flowing through the chakras can to some extent be directed through deep breathing combined with creative visualization. These exercises impel you to think increasingly in terms of light and radiance from within, rather than in terms of appearance only. You become an originator of causes rather than a manipulator of effects, and so increase the ratio of voluntary to involuntary behavior in your life. Glands, or chakras, are destiny, but their operations are not altogether beyond your power to influence.

Breathing exercises, called pranayama, not only affect the forces which compose your visible form, but they vivify and repattern certain more subtle elements that form the matrix out of which your body is shaped. This network of conditioning energies is usually termed the etheric body. Eastern students of yoga know it as the "pranamaya kosha" or vital sheath. The tangible physical organism is never considered to be an initiating cause, but only a terminus in a chain of effects working outward from subtle to increasingly material planes of consciousness. Thus the etheric body represents the missing link between physical and mental sheaths. In its understanding and control lies the formula for healing the split between body and mind.

An old Hindu parable illustrates the far-reaching effects of the breath in unifying the multiple aspects of our nature.

A certain prime minister, having fallen into disfavor with his king was, as punishment, confined at the top of a tall tower. One night his disconsolate wife crept to the foot of the tower to console him. He instructed her to fetch a horned beetle, a dab of honey, and lengths of thread, string, twine and rope. On her return with these items he had her smear the honey on the insect's horns and point it up the tower. The beetle, following the scent before it, crawled up to the high window pulling the thread behind. Grasping the thread the prisoner was able to raise successively the string, twine and rope. He then climbed down the rope to freedom.

This tale symbolizes the need for connections between the positive male principle at the top of the tower (or spine) and the negative female principle below. It also shows that the physical act of breathing is like the thread which affects the nervous system. Nerves, in turn, conduct the electricity or prana that galvanizes the body. The pranic forces are directed by the mind. Once they have been connected, as was the thread, string, twine and rope, we can find our way to freedom from the fortress of the body.

The fact that the respiratory system is closely allied with the nervous system is recognized by modern physicians, as well as the ancient gurus who called breathing exercises "nerve purifying" because they were supposed to cleanse the "nadis" or conduits through which nervous impulses pass. The real aim of deep breathing was to stimulate nerves and brain. We know that nerves serve as transmitters for thought processes. But just how this translation of mental impulses into neural synapses occurs is still a mystery because the existence of the intermediary etheric body, in the individual or in the cosmos, has not been generally accepted. Science still seeks to explain the connections between thought and action, but can say little about the process except that it has something to do with electrical impulses.

Whereas Western thinkers have tended to see human personality as clearly divided into mind and matter, whereas the yogis have always believed that man has not just one body, but a whole succession of interconnected sheaths or vehicles, through which the divine spirit (called atma) operates. These subtle gradations of consciousness form a continuous extension of spiritual essence into the myriad manifestations of matter. They are as follows:

1. Annamaya kosha: Gross physical body
2. Pranamaya kosha: Subtle or etheric body
3. Manomaya kosha: Desire-Mind body
4. Vijnanamaya kosha: Higher mind, body of wisdom
5. Anandamaya kosha: Body of bliss

The purpose of yoga is to refine and align these vehicles so that the inner splendor may shine through. This results in an analogous refinement and alignment of the forces of the physical body which reflects the subjective structure of being, as a shadow projected on the ground would give a rough idea of the structure of the building casting that shadow. If the bodies are visualized as horizontal layers or planes of consciousness, then the chakras are the vertical lines of connection enabling force to flow through from one level to another.

An interesting analogy to the individual's efforts to utilize the potential latent in the *atma* is found in the release of the energy locked within the *atom*. In order to achieve self-realization the yogi must experience the truth that matter and spirit are one. In order to harness atomic power the formula had to be found that would similarly demonstrate that matter and energy are one.

Although scientists are quick to admit that they don't know exactly what electricity is, they know enough about it to prove that all matter is, in its basic organization, electrical and convertible into energy. At approximately the same time this reve-lation revolutionized the world of physics, psychologists taking their cue from Freud, affirmed that all human instincts arise from a similar reservoir of energy called the libido. Libido is, in its broadest sense, sex, the sacred fire, or Kundalini. Sex was realized to be not a blind urge that, like lightning, might hap-hazardly strike, but the very foundation of our psyche.

The extent to which modern atomic physics has given us a vision of the world, as composed of infinitely varied vibratory modulations, has made it easier for us to comprehend arcane concepts of yoga formerly considered esoteric and divulged only to the initiated few. In Sanskrit, the original language of yoga, there are more words for religious and philosophic con-cepts than exist in Greek, Latin and German combined. For centuries there was no popularly available language to express such abstract subtleties of thought, and the yoga tradition passed through a period of latency. Now, contemporary science is giving us a new terminology, not only of words but of basic concepts. It is easier to understand a vortex if you have seen a whirlpool, or to comprehend telepathy in an age of radios. Likewise our knowledge of electricity may reveal to us what sex really means in the dynamics of self and universe.

The brain radiates waves, but every other zone of the body also emits measurable vibrations showing vortices of force at just those spots where yogis have long claimed to perceive sensi-tive centers of reception and transmission in the human body. Already some scientists are able to study the pulsations of force along the main nerve channels and to diagnose diseases by re-cording changes in the body's electrical potential. According to the unified field theory the laws of electromagnetism apply equally to an atom or a galaxy. An even more significant sci-entific breakthrough may be achieved when these same funda-mental laws are extended inward to include the psychology of all sentient creatures, unifying animate and inanimate beings within a single bipolar scheme.

Now that we have a science of supersonics, and speak casual-ly of infrared and ultraviolet ranges of light, it may be easier to accustom ourselves to the idea of bodies beyond the body. Then we will be in a position to investigate such subjects as bilocation, astral projection, survival of death and reincarnation which are bound to transform our outlook on sex, disease, morality and mortality. Birth control pills have rendered obsolete old standards of sexual behavior. But we must have an altogether new view of sex and destiny if we are to learn how to make the most of our new found freedom to love without pain. Mankind is at last ripe for a resurgence of yoga which is no longer just a light emerging out of the East, but, like the midday sun, should illumine all our horizons.

Yoga means the unification of self and source. It refers also to the diverse methods which seekers of all races and religions have employed in the search for integration. It is both the means of our regeneration and the ultimate end. The goal is achieved when ends and means are known as one. Yoga is a "way of life" and this way is a path, not to travel, but to become.

3

Sex and Sublimation

GREAT LOVERS ARE NEVER FAT. Castrates are rarely thin. Between baby fat and middle-aged spread there unfolds that delightful period when youth vibrates to youth, with bodies both firm and flexible, slim and supple, taut and elastic, stretching like strings of a lute resounding the note of love.

How then does it often happen that the flower-soft maidens toughen into aggressive, frizzy-haired and hoarse-voiced matrons, while their rugged partners yield passively to become their mild, silently resigned shadows? Presumably they still have sex together, perhaps because books say it's good for them, perhaps because habit has its hold on them.

One of the greatest things about sex is self-discovery. In love we experience our own capacity to relate and to see ourselves mirrored in another's eyes. The already urgent biological drive in the young is intensified by the fact that they are undergoing what psychologists refer to as the "identity crisis." Thus they are doubly primed to achieve the overwhelming and eternally true insight, that it is most possible to find oneself in the act of giving oneself away, and that expressing one's unique individuality means seeking completion in another.

Eating, on the other hand, no matter how convivial the company, is essentially for ourselves alone. Maybe that is why we crave company at mealtimes and desire to make them social occasions, something that is certainly not likely to happen in our sex lives. Nobody else can so intimately savor the taste of a piece of pie as oneself, especially after holding back all evening for a midnight raid on the refrigerator. Since it is all up to us, we may even be tempted to add that left-over slice of cake. Then come the regrets because, of course, everybody can see that these left-overs have left themselves over us in unseemly bulges. Only with sex can we eat our cake and have it, too, again and again.

The truly dismaying thing about fat is that with advancing years, it not only obliterates individuality and makes one look like all other fat people, but it also disguises sex. The obese man's hips and breasts develop, the woman's waist and the proud lift of her chin sink into folds of flesh, while little though she may care to admit it, a bulge is not a curve.

An oversimplified but noteworthy division of the population can be made into food people and sex people. With aging, representatives of the second category tend to flow into the first. These contrasting types may start from the same point when the basic appetites of youth are mutually compatible. Ultimately, however, there comes a fork in the road through life, when it becomes necessary to decide which kind of person one determines to be. The choice becomes increasingly obligatory, since fat not only makes sex less esthetically pleasurable, but diminishes desire. Refusing to decide is also a decision of a kind, but doubly negative, since it can result in losing out both ways.

Part of the difficulty arises from the fact that sex is often a forbidden fruit, while the lure of food is both approved and available. When food, too, must be sacrificed for the sake of some diet — well, breaking the rules makes a relatively harmless substitute for those other unobtainable delights. Besides, food usually turns out to be cheaper in the end. Sometimes it seems "nicer" because it has to do with the top, rather than that other part of the body. And if an extra drink or dessert argues back, one can at least swallow a pill which is easier than swallowing bitter words from a lover or mate.

Even language conspires to give food the edge. One's beloved may be sweetheart, honey, sugar, apple of one's eye, delectable, or delicious, inspiring the desire to eat up, chew, bite, nibble or consume. But how often is food called dear or darling, much less orgiastic or ravishing? One can "devour" one's partner with kisses or even a hungry look, but who ever raped a hamburger?

The instinct to eat insures personal survival, while the instinct to reproduce insures survival of the race. With food we stamp our identity on space; with sex we extend it into time. We don't have to fret about nations being deprived of sex, nor about the world becoming depopulated (unless the eaters become so numerous someone feels compelled to start dropping bombs). But lack of food is an ever-present issue that takes precedence over all else.

The complementary nature of these two urges sets up an uneasy balance in world societies and economies. Excessively populated areas are rarely composed of fat citizens, certainly not in Asia and parts of South America. The overproduction of offspring is just about the most effective means yet devised for depleting physical and personal resources. In countries such as the United States where birth control is becoming the rule, obesity constitutes an urgent national problem, condoned only by food and garment industries. Modern industrial nations which produce an ever-swelling torrent of goods also have a better chance of accommodating their populations. The entire affair seems almost hydraulic. You push something in here and it pops out there. Limit creation of babies and individuals grow fat. Limit or contain population growth and the race is in danger of growing mentally and morally flabby from over-indulgence in a surfeit of consumable products.

There is a way out, however, and like the way out of all vicious circles it has to be up. Intellectually creative couples produce an average of fewer than three children and, according to surveys and common observation, are far more likely to be slender than members of less privileged groups. They have other interesting pastimes on which to expend their energies besides eating and increasing the size of their family. They are engaged in producing children of the mind and spirit.

Somehow, high status people have always managed to enjoy sex without excessive childbearing and good food without corpulence. Thus they end up with that greatest of all luxuries — health. Not only do they acquire more and better things, but also the leisure, taste and sensitivity to enjoy them. Like trees that have managed to grow higher than the forest ceiling, they receive most of the sunshine and so flourish above all the others, illustrating the old proverb, "Unto them that hath it shall be given." Their disciplined lives lead not to denial but to greater freedom and fulfillment.

Living in a democracy points up the fact that basic differences exist inside people and are not just a function of social or economic standing. Real intelligence and creativity can be as much a cause, as effect of status. The fact that privileged people are far more likely to be slender than the underprivileged is one of the obvious and undeniable facts of present social patterns. Certain societies (where the masses of people are deprived) have taken opulent proportions as a desirable sign of prosperity and success, yet one rarely envisions aristocrats or heroes as being fat.

The pathetic feature of our food-oriented culture is that there does not seem to be any real enjoyment or enduring satisfaction in the common propensity to be incessantly licking ice cream, sucking through straws, chewing gum, crunching or munching candy, peanuts, popcorn or potato chips, smoking, drinking, talking of eating, or in the preoccupation with delectable maidens advertising bosoms, lipsticks, beverages, and all enticements designed for conspicuous and never ceasing consumption.

Some psychologists have blamed this blatant orality and dependence on mother surrogates upon the custom of early weaning. It might also stem from our unrealized estrangement from Mother Nature and our consequent deprivation of all that is natural such as fresh air, beautiful scenery, walks in the country, association with animals, watching things grow, solitude and repose.

The characteristics of the so-called materialist, his preoccupation with elaborate food, drink and the indulgence of every desire, are not the traits of one who has any real love for materials themselves, or for that portion of matter encompassed by his own skin. Such types are more noted for their waste and disregard of nature's handiwork and for cynical self-destruction. Their natural habitat is the bar, night club, or restaurant, and their well-shod feet rarely touch the earth but remain insulated by layers of asphalt or concrete. In their lives they move from box to box, that is, from apartment to car, subway or bus, school, shop or office, and back again. To the very end they are always in some sort of rectangular compartment.

Most of their cravings are not really tactile at all but are in the mind. Hence their preference for products whose external smoothness, gloss, whiteness or fancy packaging deflects attention from the fact that they contain practically no real value or nutrition. These novelties are so empty within they can never give the satisfaction promised and the consumer must have more and more. In this way people grow fat, beefy and stiff, not because they are greedy, but because the body can't obtain the vital substances that sustain life.

On the other hand, the visionary or dreamer, the very one whom some contemptuously call the "starry-eyed idealist," longs to see matter glorified and used appreciatively. Out of such dreams grow works of art, hospitals, parks and universities. Often the vision becomes so real that the individual who labors for its materialization can not afford to allow the body to be a less than efficient instrument in accomplishment of the work at hand.

One group of people who tend to be well in control of their bodies are the artists. While gifted and creative people may be far from models of decorum, as children of nature they often retain a youth and zest that eludes the average, solid, work-a-day citizen. This is true not just of actors, dancers and movie stars, but of those who work with fabrics, clay, paint, words, music, and even of craftsmen and technicians whose feeling for the materials of their trade gives them a sense of form and proportion. It happens, at least, if they are original, not just in producing something that looks different, but in delving back to the origin and source of their own creativeness.

This is not just a hypothetical example or general impression. In years of conducting health, yoga and exercise classes, we have found that the overwhelming majority of individuals who were attracted to, and proved willing to persist in these physical disciplines, were artists by profession or hobby, or were in some way leading uncommonly creative lives. The average housewife, businessman or laborer would rather bulge than budge to undertake so strenuous a routine. The artistic types seemed more than usually resilient and well-built, and they were willing to work on the body just as they would on a picture, poem or lump of clay. They were accustomed to the idea of transforming substance rather than passively drawing on it, and could apply this dynamic attitude to themselves. They had faith in their own ability to produce results.

The physical attractiveness of the artistically inclined students seemed to show more than just an enhanced sensuousness of response to form. In their intense creativity they re-created their own selves almost as a byproduct. This vital power had little to do with food to which, in their inspired moments, they could seem remarkably indifferent. They had a quality that was virtually electric which kept them galvanized, as though they drew their energy from some ethereal source.

We would say that these highly productive people were sex-rather than food-oriented, not just because they usually enjoyed good sexual relationships but because of an aura of romance engendered by their ability to participate in and share the feelings of others — in short, simply to love. Just as sex has both generative and regenerative aspects so, too, the will to create can be a higher expression of the desire to procreate. Anyone who has ever produced a poem, story, song or object of exceptional beauty knows that the joy of bringing something new and lovely into existence affords a rapture far more akin to the ecstasy of love, than to the placid satisfactions of the dinner table.

SEX AND SUBLIMATION / 167

The reason for this subtle electrification is that artistic creation, like procreation, demands polarity. There must be both the positive vision and the negative material waiting to be shaped, the seed and the earth in which it is implanted. In the creative individual male and female poles tend to coexist, hence the association of artistic temperament with boys wearing long hair and girls attired in pants. Interestingly enough, the fact that it sometimes is hard to distinguish between the boys and the girls has never seemed to interfere with their love life, whose freedom reflects nature's unstinting abundance more than restrictive social mores.

Among men, however, the real poets and artists are seldom as effeminate as some might presume from their flowing locks and refined mannerisms, and a girl reputed to be a tomboy can be all female when she chooses, even if too wrapped up in her work to don the hat and gloves of formal society. Tomboys have been said to make the best wives, and possibly their sufficiency and taste for simplicity takes many a burden off a hard-working husband.

Even those artists who appear downright androgynous are, for the most part, sex- rather than food-type people. They show an empathy for both male and female outlooks which affords them the psychological acumen that has made them especially renowned in the world of the theatre. The entirely oral or food-dependent person must always be in search of new distractions to compensate for his sense of personal incompleteness, and so has neither the time nor the capacity for the solitude required to give birth to new and remarkable creations.

Creative ability is, of course, far from being a special prerogative of so-called Bohemian types, even though genius has always been associated with a certain degree of personal eccentricity and disregard for convention. Yet the greatest men have usually been known as "gentle" men, intuitive thinkers, sensitive, cultivated, and often remarkably tender and considerate in their private lives. If asked to name a list of the world's outstanding benefactors, most people will include more artists, philosophers and humanitarians than generals. Even a scientific genius like Einstein was hardly the rugged "he-man" considered the male ideal, and he achieved his most illuminating insight into the theory of relativity while pushing a baby carriage in the park.

Most famous statesmen have served as protectors of their people rather than instigators of battle. Their accomplishments flow from pens rather than guns. Mahatma Gandhi who led India's freedom fight was primarily concerned with nonviolence. He was an ardent believer in vegetarianism and a devoted nurse to the sick. When we pay the high compliment of saying that a man is "Christ-like" we are not thinking of how typically male he is. Excessive virility may produce babies, but not much that uplifts the spirit. How much after all does the average soldier or athlete contribute to the evolution of the race?

On the distaff side, the greatest women have never been those who gave birth to the most babies or kept the tidiest houses with the whitest wash. More often they were fighters for some unpopular cause, battling aggressively in spite of criticism and setbacks. Florence Nightingale, Maria Montessori, Eleanor Roosevelt, Margaret Sanger, Indira Gandhi and other women such as these have needed the firmest strength and conviction to accomplish the good they wrought and to show that it was not unwomanly to struggle and conquer in the arena of the world.

A way to diagram the situation is to draw a circle and label the top male and the bottom female. On the left or negative side we find the sexes merging indistinguishably into an amorphous and distinctly unattractive form of homosexuality. Here we have the fat varieties of the "fairy" or "queer" in the "faggot," and the coarseness of the "butch" in the lesbian relationship. The personalities on the negative side of the circle often degenerate into sado-masochism, dope, drink and revolting perversions. The depressing thing about such people is not that they may be doing something morally wrong, but that they lead such ugly, miserable and twisted lives. Having no roots they become parasites on others, and hence their pathological jealousy and insecurity. Little wonder that their bodies turn gross and shapeless, since there is no inner structure to give support.

On the right, positive and integrative side, we have the man who is more than a man, adding to his male traits an almost maternal solicitude for others. Here, too, is the woman who can not only run a house and raise children, but who has the grit and determination to stand up and fight for her beliefs, often incurring the enmity of other women in daring to jump beyond the feminine role. These superior individuals are apt to be even more misunderstood than the inferior types since they represent the future rather than the past. They serve as exemplars, not of the lack of sexual differentiation, but of the reunion of opposites separated in the course of evolution.

Everyone requires and produces hormones of the opposite sex to be physically complete. In like manner we require certain qualities customarily associated with the opposite sex to become fully productive members of society. Men are often attracted by women who have their own careers and who are capable of understanding male problems, while women are apt to be smitten by the charms of poets, artists and smooth or sympathetic kinds of men.

There appears to be a higher or positive type of bisexual who can be outstandingly creative. In the Orient the Buddhas and certain Hindu deities are explicitly hermaphroditic. Our hypothetical circle can also be filled in with every conceivable intermediary variation. Nor is the process static. Individuals can deteriorate or move toward redemption. The fundamental fact remains that it is possible to be male or female *plus* something of the opposite sex, without sacrificing potency or glamour.

Keeping both poles of the psychic battery system active generates an inner current which can empower us to illumine the self and enlighten the world.

We now have some clue as to why seeming homosexuals have achieved such extraordinary success in the fields of the theatre, dance, fashion, hairdressing, photography and social reporting, and why these media have wrought such remarkable modifications in the shapes of those who aspire for status and popularity. Homo or hetero, the preoccupation is still sexual in contrast to the food- and mouth-centered indulgences that betoken a more sedentary way of life. Wearing short, tight skirts, being photographed in fashionable places, participating in the "in" sports of skiing and surfing, dancing in a discotheque and behaving like one of the jet set, demands a "go-go" figure never required by old-time petticoats.

Much criticism has been made of the fact that the world of women's fashions seems to be dominated by effeminate males with a penchant for boyishly shaped models, but this has certainly helped to instill a healthy ideal of slimness into an over-indulgent society. It would take a carping critic to say that many of these streamlined "beauties" are not sexually attractive, in spite of the athleticism suggested by long legs and slim flanks.

Much of the reaction seems to depend on whether one goes in for legs or bosoms! In recent times an advocate of the enormous bosom has been *Playboy Magazine,* and now the main function of its "bunnies" is to sell food and drinks at clubs around the nation. The indeterminately-sexed lords of fashion may have become whipping boys for the bountiful bosom set, but for all their freakish get-ups, devised largely for publicity, they have certainly slimmed us down drastically, and are in no danger of being dethroned.

So to those of you who want to stay slender and chic, we say, take the hint. Better still, take up weaving, sculpting, writing, dancing, traveling, making rugs, candles, stone rubbings, social work or anything utilizing mental potential. Don't just collect or rearrange objects, try to put something new into the world which not only develops your talent but has, at least, the possibility of bringing joy to others.

Just because you are a woman, don't consider it necessary to stick to fancy cooking and embroidery while your husband watches the ball game. Let him have some fun in the kitchen (you can remind him that the best chefs are men) while you try taking an adult education course. At least *try* something unusual and different. Those men who feel sheepish about experimenting with clay or color might recollect that the world's most renowned artists have been men, and that such successful figures as Churchill and Eisenhower have refreshed themselves by daubing paint, and done it well. By and large it has been men who have created the jewelry, perfumes, styles, and coiffures that make women more feminine. Especially in France where men pride themselves on being accomplished lovers, the feminine art of sexual allure has been cultivated. But France also produced a galaxy of powerful women writers — and Joan of Arc.

Observe your gifted and artistic friends and notice how youthful and vital they remain. Make it a point to cultivate this kind of person. Love and help them without criticizing their clothes, hair or romances. Be graceful, spontaneous, and above all enjoy — remembering that to en-joy means literally to put joy into. This is not the same as happiness. One can be unhappy about all sorts of calamities, and still, on a higher level, experience the joy of knowing oneself to be essentially a free spirit.

With or without a mate, sublimate and have a love affair with the world, or even with a rough clay mug shaped by hand. Such diversions do not mean settling for second best but ingeniously pursuing more varied and enduring satisfactions. Consider sending your libido back to the university of the universe for advanced studies. Discover how many good and pleasing courses it offers besides the ones served on your dinner table, or even intercourse. Relate, create, have an enthusiastic regard for all the world, and thus reflect the youth and loveliness which nature ever brings to birth. This is the power that makes all things new. It is yours. Use it and give it forth again.

PART FIVE

Philosophy of Weight Control

1

Gratitude

TO GROW A BODY; THIS IS A COMPLICATED PROCESS. Yet it comes to us so easily. It is the easy things we complicate, such as how to use the resources so freely given. We forget that the word "re-source" implies that we should attach ourselves not to isolated things but to the source from which they have been bestowed.

The problem is not how to receive. Taking comes to us naturally. We can not avoid drawing in and absorbing the universal life-force with every breath our lungs inhale. The question is how to increase our giving in order to clear away space to receive more abundantly. This returns us to our original premise that we can have whatever is needed and suitable to our requirements, providing we know how to give it away again.

The time to review our eating habits, and the way of life they reflect, comes when we find ourselves adding to our bodies more than they can burn up or eliminate. Every creature functions in the same basic threefold manner, receiving, assimilating, and transmitting a portion of the vital and material substance of the universe. This is the law of all creation. We are enabled to function creatively, not by producing something out of nothing, but through *participation* in the ceaseless interchange of elements. We grow not by accumulating diverse materials, but by integrating them into the pattern of our lives. They must be part of ourselves before we can give them to others.

How, then, are we to reverse the grasping tendency of our socially conditioned avarice and realize that it is indeed more blessed to give than to receive? More blessed because the receiving is as natural and unavoidable as it is for earth to accept the rain, and trees the sunlight. It is through the deliberate cultivation of giving that we develop the sense of purpose which makes us truly human. A person who cooks for others, supports a family, sends food to the needy or invests in some worthy enterprise is bound to have to consider the motivation and intent of his offering, and thus come to know himself better.

All beings transform energy into substance and substance into energy. Man's part in this process is to perform the function consciously with specific goals in mind. Just as plants blend two opposing streams or directional tendencies, by raising nutrients from the earth below while photosynthesizing sunshine from above, so does man transmute food from the earth into mental illumination, while simultaneously directing his enlightened mind toward the building of matter into more intricate forms.

To be human is to stand between heaven and earth, eternally stretched between contrasting poles, and blending them. The opposites which rend us asunder can make us stronger as we strive to resolve harmony out of conflict and stamina out of stress. We must expend in order to expand, become independent to realize our involvement, and serve all to master ourselves.

We set this reciprocal process in motion by giving, and the first thing we have to donate is gratitude for all that has been received. How else could we have anything to dispense? This offering of thanks betokens a graciousness which makes us great in heart as well as graceful in form.

By sitting down to a meal with the plaintive sigh, "Is this all I am getting?" a sense of deprivation is inculcated which nothing can satisfy. But by being thankful for that which *has* been granted, even the small miracle of a bowl of soup opens the way into a realm of divine plenitude.

The sense of abundance can be cultivated just as you might learn to play a piano or master a language—through the practice of specific techniques. These methods can be as dependable as exercises by which muscles and minds mature. They begin with the fine art of appreciation.

First you can dwell on the nature of the food itself — its taste, texture and the delightfulness of its presence on the dinner table. Consider the care taken to procure it and all the preparation that has taken place in the kitchen, the market and on the way to market. Ruminate upon the complexity of the ingredients brought together for even a light repast. Ponder what millennia of experience were required to learn to harvest, combine and serve these artfully blended substances. Imagine being a primitive person and trying to *invent* bread or deciding what to do with a field of wheat. Maybe they were smarter than we think.

Notice the service. Does the fine china and delicate crystal reflect the elegant slenderness and refinement recognized as signs of good breeding? Or maybe one reason for the habitual culinary restraint that well-to-do people are likely to practice is that at a beautifully appointed dinner table, there are many gratifying items, other than food, to seduce the senses. An artistic floral centerpiece, candles, table linen, background music, the view from a window, curtains, pictures on the wall, lively conversation and, above all, the company of congenial personalities can so amply nourish the soul that the body rests content.

Satisfaction also springs from simplicity. The Japanese in their ritual tea ceremony may take an hour or more to consume a single cup of tea. They find silence, emptiness and meditation more harmonious than the elaborate decor of the occidental-style dining room. Either way tastefulness satisfies taste.

By contrast the image of the habitual overeater is far more likely to be that of someone always with a hot dog, doughnut or candy bar in hand. Fat people rarely seem to overindulge at the dinner table but are to be found later in the evening obsessively stuffing the mouth with food, or else picking away nervously at leftovers. The housewife's nemesis is the children's uneaten peanut butter sandwich she is too frugal to waste and eats on the run, not the consommé, salad and soufflé she whips together for a fancy luncheon.

Appreciation can extend as far as the mind can reach, and then some, stretching thought to new horizons. Encouraging the imagination to range in search of more distant antecedents and origins can be a great liberating force in the development of higher sensibilities, even leading to the unfoldment of intuitive capacities ordinarily considered paranormal.

Reflect, for example, on the care taken in growing the oranges and coffee beans that contribute toward what might formerly have seemed a skimpy breakfast. Visualize the people who picked and sorted these products of the distant tropics, the placid cow giving milk for your tea or coffee, the lush fields of cane from whence came your sugar. If you eat honey, remember the bees, the bright flowers or clover in which they feed. You may find yourself preferring healthier vegetarian foods as you increase your sensitivity to what they are. Nuts and fruits evoke prettier pictures than kidneys and tripe.

Then realize that all the pleasures in which you are partaking were freely provided by nature and its creatures. Reflect upon the miracle of growth, how black soil and golden sunshine, blue sky and green leaves combine to produce the multi-hued fruits of earth. In meditating upon the presence of such a wonder as an orange, one might almost forget to eat! Then if the body remains in genuine need, allow the appetite its due. At least there will not be a delusive mentalized craving for unnecessary nourishment because the mind is indulging in its own proper satisfactions. It is lust after food which by its compulsiveness tends toward excess. Real love for food is salutary since we do not misuse what we really cherish.

Appreciation may be extended through many commonplace activities. Say a mental thank you when you cash a check or carry a load of groceries from the market. Soon this will become a habitual attitude, no more trouble than a smile. This is not a self-conscious pose or artificial flattery of some god to be propitiated. Rather, such gratitude serves as a psychic lever to release a shower of benefits out of nature's limitless supply. It is not only a result but an initiating cause of abundance, not only a thank you for help received but a power by which help is invoked.

Attention can be drawn inward with each mouthful chewed, as you admire the efficiency with which the cells of your body break down, sort out and absorb the digested food particles until they are part of *you,* your body, your mind, this thinking in which you are now engaged. How does it happen that a lowly carrot or potato can become a great idea? Can we, too, be fodder for some grand consummation? Never mind if your thoughts run on fantastically. Those which are wise will be assimilated.

This propensity for loosing the imagination to brood over the origins and significance of objects perceived does not make them blurry with associations but brings them into sharper focus. Suddenly the whole world becomes more effulgent. Familiar things take on a crystalline sheen as with new inclusiveness you encompass them with your comprehension. Mundane events shine with unexpected significance. Ecstasy lies just around the corner; each raindrop is a coruscating lens of heaven and the merest mud puddle an eye of all the sky. Simply to sense is to be continuously amazed with new revelations.

This same technique of penetrating to the heart of things in order to see life whole can prove remarkably fruitful in problem-solving activities. Allow your mind to brood reflectively over the issue at hand like a mother hen, and when the time is ripe the unyielding shell will, of its own accord, crack open and offer its contents. Inventive people are unanimous in agreeing that when the need for a new concept arises, it is better, after having done one's best, to cease laboring over it and consign it to the subjective department of the mind until it ripens spontaneously and, at the propitious moment, presents itself for birth.

To analyze is not the same as to think creatively. When you start weighing your thoughts about yourself, try not to pick away at deficiencies. Rather see yourself as you might be, and as you were *intended* to become. Can you use your new found powers of appreciation to be grateful for yourself and all that your being on earth represents? Certainly, if you have learned to respond to the remarkable properties of coffee beans and oranges, you can do as much for a human body and soul, even your own. Try to allow nature her due for creating you. Surely there must have been some purpose in it.

Dancers usually have lovely figures, not just because they exercise, but because they have learned how to enjoy having a body and using it gracefully. Conversely, some people with theoretically good proportions appear stiffly bound, encased by tensions and obstructed in motion. Often the loss of beauty associated with aging reflects this rejection of the body, a scorn which justifies the spurious pleasures of unrestrained eating.

Few children, unless subjected to the fears and frustrations of their elders, are either stiff or fat. Try to recollect being a child and how keen your feelings were. Remember how you could delight in a pair of new shoes, or a field of buttercups, or a good grade in school. That is why the memories of childhood persist and sometimes grow stronger with age. You were so alive! If food could taste as it did at five or ten, who would need to overeat? If exercise could feel as exhilarating we would still be skipping rope and turning somersaults. A child seldom passes value judgments on things. He does not smear the pristine face of reality with his own preconceived notions, but tends to accept life as it is.

Try to respond to the sounds and sensations, as well as to the silences and empty spaces, arising from your environment. If you do this with the spontaneity of a child's wonder and surprise, enthusiasm will follow. Be grateful for the enriching insight which your adult experience affords, but first cleanse the doors of perception and let in the light. The formula for this admission requirement is written:

Appreciation equals Attractiveness.

The first side of this equation measures your capacity to respond and project yourself outward into the world of experience. The second side shows the result which is the power to draw all good back into yourself and be transformed. Balance there must and always will be. This is the first law of nature. You need to make this balance a dynamic interaction between self and environment and not a restriction of the flux of circumstances within the mold of preconceived ideas.

Finally, in our meditation on gratitude, we can direct our thoughts forward. Toward what good end will we utilize that which we have taken for our own? What should ownership mean? We may be filled by what comes into us but we can be fulfilled only by what we give back to life. In the end our sustaining satisfactions lie neither in giving nor taking, but in mutual sharing of the overflowing abundance of nature.

2

The Power of the Will

MOST OF US BELIEVE that we can will what we do. But can we will what we will? There's the rub. Especially since the people who argue most vehemently in favor of the theory of free will are often those who make the least use of it. The pathetic helplessness of the dieter unable to restrain his appetite makes us wonder how much man can determine not just what he does, but what he is. Can we control the controller, or should we wish to?

The first point to realize about this much misunderstood quality is that will is not just strong personal desire but evidences impersonal intent. Its driving purpose can even oppose desire. You can desire mightily to push your finger through a piece of cloth, but it still won't go. Reduce the piercing area to the size of a needle's point and it penetrates effortlessly and exactly as you will it to. Will involves, therefore, some understanding of and cooperation with the laws of nature. Desire can be a wanton craving for things unlawful, but will implies the power to discern and choose what is right.

As every dieter knows, "will power" alone can never achieve long term results, if the effort is thought to involve some painful renunciation or forcing through intolerable resistance. Will is not implacable or unshakable fixity. Any improvement program undertaken with rigid inflexibility will usually fail because such unyieldingness expresses the same negativity it is necessary to overcome. Facility comes by focusing force, efficiency in ease. What we are looking for is a laser to concentrate our efforts, not a bulldozer to push harder and plow up increasing resistance.

Will may indeed prove to be the shining push button to success, but only when it is part of a circuit that is connected to a generator. If you would tap this power you must be an integrated personality, and you must be consciously aligned with your innate potential for perfection. How can a person who believes himself a wretched failure have will? What current would there be behind the push button? Without sufficient discipline and preparation, even if he could in some way hook up the wires, he would probably cause a short circuit and wreck his equipment.

In the final analysis the invocation of the will depends on this ability to tap the resources of the higher Self. It requires a keenness of intent achieved by few men. Desires, on the other hand, obscure the will and spring up like vegetation from the seeds of instincts buried below the surface of awareness. Like the creatures of the earth, desires are legion; but just as there is one sun in the sky, there is but One Will. This is the will of God, Supreme Being, or whatever you choose to call the ultimate principle of order which imbues all nature with responsive life. Through training of the will the yogi achieves divine powers, but only to the extent that he wills what God wills, and knows the two as one.

Will is unifying energy. Only when perverted does this power become regimenting, standardizing, and oppressive. The fact that men now have more freedom of will than ever before is balanced by the hardening of authoritarianism in the world, with dictatorial governments stifling individual impulses toward freedom and spontaneity.

To some extent this negative manifestation of will has come as an inevitable result of the population crisis. If two people live in a home they can do pretty much as they choose. If twenty-five people are residing in the same house there must be stringent regulations to insure fair treatment for all, and each one's free will is drastically diminished. All too often this need for consideration deteriorates into blind conformity, enforced for its own sake and not in service of the individual. Unity is *not* uniformity, but central purpose that integrates the diverse parts into an organic synthesis. Masses too easily degenerate into mobs. The promise of the one humanity lies only in the value of the individual.

Positive will requires not a stiffening of desire but the opposite ability to relax and let go. Its qualities are humor, proportion and undemanding love. Literally, to will is to be willing to do what is needed, to follow the admonitions of the Good Law by relinquishing petty egoism and selfish gratifications. It is letting go in the sense that if we do the letting, the power itself will do the going without our interference.

Will is also the future tense of "to be." It is all we can ever hope to be or become. That is the only freedom any of us can experience, the freedom to become as we truly are, to manifest the essence of our selves, just as a seed is free to flower only in its own image.

The expression of will requires not just belief in a power within, but also a conviction that good will ultimately triumph. An individual can not simply let go and be "willing" to cooperate with the dictates of nature, if nature is not his friend, daily guide, companion, or even cherished mother in whose everlasting arms all creatures eventually come to rest.

Nor do we refer to nature as some abstract principle which forces us to behave. Nature is what we are, our own body and the wisdom it contains, which is in some ways more ancient and profound than the wisdom of the ego. We may fool friends and family, but no one fools the body, at least not in the end. This is ample reason to respect it. Instead we often fight its instincts in an internecine war, hiding out behind lonely bastions of defense whose outermost ramparts are often solid layers of fat requiring the additional protection of camouflaging garments. The war against nature is the one war we are bound to lose, and in that lies our ultimate salvation.

Self-knowledge gives power and will, but this is true only if you rise high enough or delve deep enough. Superficial or cynical psychologising may just land you in the position of the suburbanite who hired a water diviner to locate a well on his property. On the spot where the divining rod began to twitch he assiduously commenced to drill — and broke into the city sewer system.

Often in tapping the shallow layers of the psyche we come to the polluted undercurrents of the mind, the aggressive fantasies, festering frustrations, perverted desires and decaying corpses of the dead past. Many modern artists and writers, in response to the psychoanalytic temper of the times, seem to have dredged up this scum from the surface of the subconscious and spread it about for display, instead of penetrating deep into the living wellsprings of the psyche.

Since the days of Sigmund Freud the unconscious mind has been berated as a scapegoat for all the naughty things we do, or wish we were doing. Yet our deepest instincts are to survive and be happy, not to do wrong. They are like the little boy who on being asked by his Sunday School teacher how to atone for sin replied, "Well, first you gotta sin."

Modern men and women do not give the impression of being unduly repressed in their sex lives, particularly the younger generation. Birth control pills will see to that. But many individuals do repress their desire for accomplishment, to find meaning in life and to serve some noble cause. They seem ashamed of their better instincts and embarrassed lest they be accused of being "do-gooders." Such denial of the possibilities of evolution, beyond socially designated goals, has not only sapped individual courage but has almost stalemated research in parapsychology with its challenging frontiers including the study of survival of death, reincarnation, healing, astral projection, clairvoyance, psychokinesis and telepathy. Academic psychology is still more "ology" than "psyche."

People sometimes try to commit suicide because consciously they have decided that life is not worth living. It is the protective instincts of the unconscious which usually hold them back and make the act seem as unnatural as deliberately ceasing to breathe. In everyday life we meet with accidents of every sort but in dreams, though we fall, we never quite hit bottom. The unconscious won't allow it.

Because the unconscious is a link to universal awareness we must take care in describing its location as up, down, or all-around. It does not really matter which way we look, because direction is only relative to the ego, pinpointed at a particular cross road of time and space, and is not relative to the all-inclusive Whole. What matters is that whichever way we look, it be with breadth of vision. There are as many stars under our feet as over our heads and off on the horizon.

It is not enough to affirm that man is potentially divine and leave it at that. Specific techniques must be devised to channel the will-to-good into peace and goodwill among men. Toward the end of the last century when that extraordinary apostle of the occult, Madame Blavatsky, burst out of her Tibetan monastery to bring the inspiration of Oriental philosophy to Europe and America, she spoke with blazing eloquence on the concept that God is a great celestial flame, and human souls like sparks cast off by this eternal combustion. On one occasion a lady came up to her and gushed, "Isn't it *wonderful* to think that I have a divine spark slumbering within my bosom!" Whereupon the redoubtable Theosophist bent toward her, finger on lips, and replied, "Shh! If you listen carefully you can hear it snoring!"

The need, therefore, is not just to repeat that most of us are better than we know, and certainly than *what* we know, but to find the specific know-how for waking up to that fact. Scientists send rockets circling through outer space, yet have little to say about how we are to lift ourselves from the surface of our superficial lives. Power to propel cars across the countryside is at our fingertips, but how do we release the powers of the soul? Houses can be illuminated by the flick of a switch, but how do we switch on spiritual illumination? Soaps and detergents by the dozens glut the market, but how do we purify our hearts? Somehow a way must be found because the only ultimate freedom any of us will ever achieve is in the control we gain over ourselves.

It is this need for a consistent plan for self-development which has led us to stress the gymnastics of the will as practiced in diet, exercise, deep breathing, relaxation and creative visualization. Providing these disciplines are sufficiently engaging they will knit you together, body and mind.

Giving to others in sympathy and love are also exercises, because to love is to heal, unify and make whole again, and so, in turn, to find ourselves beautiful and beloved. The best exercise for the heart is still to reach down and lift people up. Every thought that goes out beyond oneself also lets in a little bit of light.

It is a sign of the split between flesh and spirit that, in this age which rings with noble sentiments about the freedom of man, little is said about the freedom to have a beautiful body. All are deemed to have a right to decent shelter, clothes, even a car. What about the body which clothes, shelters and provides a vehicle for the inner self? Should not some degree of physical charm and efficiency be as inalienable a right as those idealized in the "four freedoms"? Is it not as important to us to be able to dance and play, to move with grace and abandon, as to circulate freely within the body of society? Bodily freedom is particularly meaningful because no one can give it to us. We have to earn and deserve it, as in an ultimate sense we must earn and deserve all our freedoms by living within the law. Will, law and freedom—these must always go together, since freedom of will is won only by submitting willingly to the law, and freedom itself is the final law and consummation of our striving.

One of the earliest emancipators of the race was the Babylonian statesman, Hammurabi, who lived about 1950 B.C. Before his day men could be cast into prison because they had no way of knowing the rules of a particular race or nation. Any passing stranger could be jailed for an inadvertent misstep. Once the laws were codified by Hammurabi, however, a new freedom was possible. At least it depended on choice whether the law was broken, and not on chance. Every great lawgiver since has advanced man's progress into freedom, including scientists who have revealed previously unknown laws of nature, and thinkers who elucidate the moral laws of the universe.

Ignorance of the law has never been considered a valid excuse for its infraction. It is up to the individual to find out what is right or wrong. To say that it is the law that we must learn the law is circular reasoning, like saying that the purpose of life is to discover the purpose of life. And yet the circle is nature's basic form! What it means is that in the end no one can give us the truth free, but only certain methods useful for its realization. These methods we call yoga. They lead us out to study the universe in order that we may find ourselves, and into ourselves that we may know what is truly "out there." Such techniques must be guideposts, not hitching posts, leading us forever on.

The fortunate part is that once the law is understood it no longer intrudes on your consciousness. You need not, for example, be constantly remembering how to breathe or swallow or walk. You can rest on attainment, like a certain diplomat who on being asked if it was necessary to know Latin and Greek to be a statesman replied, "No indeed, it is quite enough to have forgotten them." Actions become habitual, like taking well-worn roads instead of beating through the underbrush, and these automatic responses in turn release energy for higher exploration. The outcome of synchronizing our behavior with the laws of the universe is peace of mind, since we are no longer contending with alien forces. The will of God is our will, as we, too, create in His image.

Many sick or obese persons might just as well be in prison because that is what their body has become. Why has bountiful nature turned into so inexorable a jailer? Because they have broken some law? It must be so. To believe in effects without causes, punishment without offense, implies a universe as chaotic as society was in the days before Hammurabi, with worse dangers and more stringent limitations. Yet there is nothing in the way that animals act, plants grow, shells unfold, ice crystals form, or in any of nature's manifold designs to show that order does not inhere everywhere. The mark of the mature mind is a concern for deeper causes and an ability to grasp prevailing principles behind phenomenal effects. No one can be free in a world of chaos. Freedom comes only in responding to the dimension of wholeness which orders the world from within.

Something has to produce the distressing conditions mirrored in our bodies. The cure can never be found until we discover what this something is and cease assigning our miseries to the caprices of fate. Somehow we must awaken to ourselves and study the laws of our own nature, that we may invoke the will to become the better selves that in truth we are. The danger, however, lies in presuming that because a thing is lawful, it must also be logical in our intellectual understanding of the term logic.

What most people have been educated to think of as logic is derived from the Aristotelian view that everything must be either A or not A, and that opposites ought to be mutually exclusive. But this is only the logic of the separative ego. The psyche operates according to a different scheme. There is, therefore, a fatal fallacy in expecting that people should be logical about their eating and exercise habits when this is not the province of the rational mind.

As we have pointed out, the body is controlled mainly by the unconscious, and if you want a picture of how *that* works just remember your dreams. Yet these dreams are a legitimate part of you. You made them up without even the excuse of inter-ference from the environment. But just because the idiom of the psyche seems irrational it should not be denigrated. The same dissolution of solid boundaries and fusing of opposites is characteristic of the super-mundane realm. That is why every saint, sage and yogi *must* speak in paradoxes and why the scriptures avoid plain language in appealing to the intuition. Only the rational intellect finds it contradictory that freedom emerges from discipline, spontaneity from restraint, self-reali-zation from selflessness and power from letting go.

In short, we come once more to the law of reverse effort which has run like a binding thread through all our discussions. Negatively the law holds that when we force matters unduly, we end with the opposite of what is sought. Thus jealousy kills love, pride betrays littleness of spirit, the search for security leads us to discover just how insecure we are. Too much food does not nourish but deprives. Conversely it is the people who have in some way been deprived who habitually overeat. Such sufferers become obese not because they enjoy a good meal but because some sense of lack demands the protection of fat, even though the "protector" is the assassin lured into the citadel they would fortify. It is the same sad story of being murdered by our defenses.

When we speak of will, therefore, we are referring to the unifying purpose which makes us true to ourselves in keeping the results of our actions in line with their intent. To the extent that we are divided within ourselves we can will nothing, but remain at the mercy of blind chance. And chance is seldom particularly merciful! Only insofar as we are integrated personalities, not just brilliant intellects, can we express freedom of will in conscious control of our bodies and destinies.

3

Faith and Responsibility

IF THE OVERWEIGHT STATE COULD BE THWARTED with exhortations to diet for beauty's sake, our middle-aged female population would undergo such a transformation that it would seem as though a different race had come to inhabit the earth. If men would similarly reduce for the sake of health, a great many more members of the race would, in fact, be inhabiting the planet. Instead we have become so well-fed that among people of the world American men now rank *eighteenth* in life-expectancy and American women *tenth*. Neither the feminine desire to hold the heart of a husband with a lovable figure, nor the male's need to protect his heart in order to insure stamina to support those he loves, can avail against the "stuffing syndrome" of our Great Society.

The crux of the matter is even deeper than these major issues of beauty and health. It concerns our mental image of ourselves, and our purpose in living, caring or wanting to care what ultimately becomes of us.

Since most of us consider that we are to some degree masters of our fate, then there must be something in us capable of demonstrating mastery. If, negatively, our innate nature is sinful and the result of Adam's original sin, then what good can or should be expected of this mortal flesh? Is it worthy of redemption, or should we rather depend on an external "saviour" who will vicariously atone for our inadequacies and remove our sins from us like a divine detergent or tranquilizer?

Many people have liberalized their religion to the point where it no longer interferes with their lives and what happens to their "immortal souls" doesn't particularly bother them. Still they are subconsciously imbued with the idea that the flesh is weak and the source of many woes, that the spirit can be saved in the end, and that there exists between these two a nice neat line like the perforation in a certificate, whereby they may divide themselves off and cash in the higher part for a reward.

Good churchgoers attend services to pray for spiritual blessings, but how many would feel just a bit foolish or wicked praying for a slender beautiful body. It is all right to petition for health, but not for that state which would make such health possible. Only an atheistic country like Russia could adopt and apply the slogan, "Health is duty — disease is sabotage" and, as a matter of official policy, substitute exercise for coffee breaks in the industrial worker's daily routine.

Looking at the devout in just about any temple of worship, one finds it hard to believe that many of them would see much connection between physical and spiritual development. Actually, few churches have encouraged dancing since that incident a while back with Moses and the golden calf, although they do serve excellent suppers! Nor do clergymen, doctors, scientists and professors as a group, show the same conscientious concern for their own bodies as for the body of the congregation, of scientific data, or the body politic, in spite of the athleticism of a Billy Graham, Paul Dudley White, or the dazzlingly fit Kennedy family.

Where should our responsibility begin? The word means "ability to respond," and to be sensitive to all that goes on within and without our covering of skin. It also means to be aware of the quality we emanate which causes others to respond to us. Responsibility is the measure of our consciousness. Consciousness we define as "any entity's innate capacity for relationships."

The first response is the ability to receive messages from the cells of our own body and sense organs, telling of their craving for oxygen and milk. Gradually we focus attention on the outer world and begin to identify with external circumstances. Then, with maturity, reactions to inner and outer worlds must be harmonized in us, and this process of adjustment gives rise to the traits which characterize our unique personalities. Essentially it is still a self-knowing, for those of us who would understand the world must also try to understand ourselves, since it is our discriminating senses that bring to us the only world we ever can know.

We create worlds through our ability to perceive them. The realm we observe is nothing like the panoply of sensations that impinge upon the plant or animal, nor even quite like that registered by any other human being. It scarcely resembles the universe of electrical impulses which science has proven underlies all material manifestations, nor the equally intangible universe of cause and effect on which the philosopher speculates. And yet, somehow, all these worlds are One.

Consider that the human body is composed of trillions of sentient *living* cell entities, each one with a purpose and destiny of its own. In each is contained a microscopic amount of that most important chemical in nature known as DNA. This is the miraculous molecule within the cell nucleus which holds the key to the genetic code of life, and which is said to contain more information than a hundred textbooks filled with fine print.

This cellular intelligence is not only knowledge in the sense of information *about* things. It sums up the entire wisdom of the body gleaned from ages past and presumes a future ages hence, for it is the key to orderly and controlled growth. This is the kind of wisdom which all our texts have not been able to impart, as far as inspiring order in the body of nations and the world. Men in their basic thinking are still more taken with the glitter of assorted facts, than with their synthesis into some meaningful design. Often, our highest achievements have been spurred by the lowest exigencies of competition in the arms race, and what we feel to be a very genuine need to increase our capacity for human destruction. Science in the search for better instruments of killing has contributed as much to demolishment as to bringing men together in love. The depressing part is not that science has failed to bring peace to the world, but that most people don't even see why it *should* enrich our spiritual as well as material lives. They still see matter and spirit as two separate compartments, so that it is deemed possible for technology to serve the one and ignore the other.

There is a positive side to the picture, in that science has proven to be a great unifying force in civilization. Churchmen may utter fine phrases about the brotherhood of man and theologians proclaim that "all is one" but still they quarrel over doctrines and split into ever more divisive schisms. Religious prejudice has ever been used to foment war and justify violence. Scientists, on the other hand, are universally in accord concerning the basic laws of the universe. They have supplied us with telephones, wireless, television, aircraft and all modes of intercommunication which have, in fact, made this world one.

The problem now is how properly to apply all that science has given. It takes understanding to transmute knowledge into wisdom and proximity into love. To under-stand implies a sensitive appreciation of the unifying design that *substands* the warp and woof of circumstance, the sentient substance out of which the whole fabric of creation is woven in one seamless design. Without this responsiveness to the vital life or soul of events, all our piled up nuggets of knowledge must fall back to sand and ashes and our mighty civilization go the way of Greece and Rome.

The progress in which we take such pride has often resulted in a form of higher development at the expense of the foundation on which it is based. In Africa a group of Masai tribesmen (including several old men and a twelve-year-old) were tested for endurance. The tribesmen could stay on a treadmill for twenty-three minutes, compared to fourteen minutes for the average American college man. Two of the Masai broke the thirty-minute limit.

We are reminded also of the anthropologist who journeyed to a remote South Pacific island to study the telepathic abilities which its natives were reputed to possess. He observed that when a certain woman wished to call her husband from the other side of the island she would talk into a tree and, sure enough, he would receive the message and return. On being asked why she used a tree to communicate her thoughts, she shrugged and replied, "It's the best we poor people can do. If we were rich like you, we would use telephones."

Can we overcome the civilized idea that it is naive or unnecessary to respond to communications which come gratuitously from our deeper psyche? Often when a child in school guesses the answer to a problem, he is hushed up until he can think of a proper reason. Little credit accrues to him for grasping an idea or formula in one flash of insight, until he works it out pedestrianly, and perhaps becomes thoroughly sick of it in the process. Seldom do teachers question the assumption that logic is better than intuition, or even ask what intuition may be. Yet the world into which the student is heading is in many ways illogically run, and when he discovers that his tools of rationality do not suffice in coping with situations which arise, he may be in trouble.

For present purposes, we define intuition as the use of the *whole* mind. It involves a willingness to accept and observe even those elements which do not fit in with a preconceived scheme of how things ought to behave. Take dreams, for example. We may reject them at first as an adult would toss aside a worthless pebble which a child has found on the beach and thinks beautiful. The pebble may indeed be of no more significance than a million others, but if the child is encouraged in his interest, he may grow in discrimination and learn to spot valuable treasures tossed up by the sea. The psyche is like a child, able to bring us gifts if we will remain open to the offer.

The same courtesy can be extended to the body itself. Only to the extent that we, as self-aware individuals, respond to the subliminal cry from all the multitudes of cells within us, and demonstrate our deep concern for their complex social welfare, their needs and idealism, can we prove ourselves responsible for the condition in which they find themselves enmeshed. Truly we are as a god to them. In us they must forever live and move and have their being. Do we show ourselves as benevolent deities? Are we to them all that we would like our god to be to us? Or are we more like a wrathful Jehovah? Can they proclaim of us, "Our God is love."

Many idealists speak of the "divine nature of man," but appear to limit this concept of divinity to a vague ghost of a "soul" which presumably floats about over our heads like a balloon. What good, one wonders, is this kind of semi-attached soul going to do anyone, until he is dead and goes drifting off in it to some celestial realm? What if by misadventure he misplaces it along the way? Yet here we are all the time, even the least of us already full-fledged gods in the amazing universe of our own body where every inhabitant is compelled to defer to all we decree. *Universe* means everywhere turning toward the one. Do we as unifier inspire chaos or harmony in these trusting cell lives?

If we who are responsible to these hard-working, long suffering multitudes laboring in the dark, not just in head and heart, but in our gall-bladder, intestines and all sorts of disagreeable places, do not give them cause to trust in us, then how can we have the conceit to pray in turn to some bigger God who rules over the heavens, and in whose judgment we as cells in the body of humanity must trust? Can we humbly beseech Him for justice and mercy and then turn around and mistreat our own bodies with no mercy or justice at all? If, on the other hand, we could really be good to ourselves, might not the blessings of divine favor come without our petitioning? After all, we can *do* something about our plight here and now, any time we will. We need not wait for this higher God to be merciful, for His doing may take much time and seems quite beyond our control. Maybe in the end we would even find that all the Gods are One?

If a devil does exist, then his chief work must be to confound the ideas of Self and selfish in men's minds. The evil is not that one can be too good to oneself and thereby false to others. It is rather in thinking that we can help ourselves without also helping our fellow men, or thinking that there can be any real difference between the two attitudes. In serving the world we must be serving ourselves. To be uplifted we must uplift others with whom we are involved. It is not the physical senses which delude as much as the sense of separativeness.

Our saving grace is the capacity for perceiving relationships and not just isolated truths. Any truth unrelated to some broader context is not just useless but meaningless, and may as well be integrated into a structure of falsity. Thus, laws no longer subsumed to an overall concern for justice, but upheld for their own sake, inevitably become oppressive. Each situation is different and demands a fresh interpretation. The law can never be wholly computerized but will always require judges as well as judgment. This is why it is said that attitudes are more important than facts. Attitudes determine the kind of facts we will select, and how we choose to place them as building blocks within our temple of wisdom.

It took men centuries to perceive the relationship between dirt and disease. Dr. Semmelweis was driven to madness and death in his fruitless attempts to persuade doctors to wash their hands between performing autopsies and delivering babies. Not until Pasteur rudely broke up a meeting of medical men by insisting on using the blackboard to draw pictures of the microbes he saw under his microscope, was there any admission that germs caused disease, even though ten women in a row had just died in the same hospital of childbed fever. Indeed, it was not the physicians and their drugs (heroic as they have been) who put an end to the worst plagues of the human race, but the sanitary engineers.

In the same way we can be sure that our mental diseases will not diminish until we give more credence to the sanitary engineers of the mind. For millennia bacteria were not accepted, simply because they were unseen. Yet their effects were real enough. Invisible but no less lethal viruses of jealousy, suspicion, criticism and resentment also cause diseases as fearful as any medieval plague and in the end may underlie all sicknesses whether of the body or mind. What we must seek now are the "germs" of the germs.

It is unlikely that physicians will achieve any spectacular success in curing obesity, sexual problems, cancer, premature aging, or any of the truly *fundamental* ills which beset us until the public is willing to do something about cleaning up the sources of psychic pollution which poison our lives at the roots. Everyone who reads a daily newspaper suspects that the world is sick. But most of us do not care to do much more than express shock and dismay, because if we are to search out the real trouble we must begin with ourselves.

Primitive peoples have generally believed in their own strict version of cause and effect. When a member of a tribe sickened or died, it was assumed to be the result of some invisible ray or influence sent out by a magician, evil-wisher or star. Then, for a long period, men had no explanation for disease except as a visitation of divine disfavor or a caprice of fate. Now, on a higher turn of the spiral, we are back to the condition of feeling oppressed with the fears of unseen rays let loose by evil-wishers, except that we have up-to-date names for them such as "fall out" and "radio-activity." And, of course, we are in a better position to demonstrate that they actually do kill people. Indeed, if they were not killers would we have worked so feverishly to release them?

Unpleasant as is the prospect of being sizzled without even knowing it, we are at least better able to think in terms of subtle forces lying behind the shifting surface of events. We know there is a world of vibration, radiation and scintillating light, and that this light-realm is also real in its effects.

If a group of people, crowded on a bus, taking a long and arduous journey, were asked where they were going and for what purpose, and they replied that not only did they not know, but they had never particularly cared to find out, one would have cause to be amazed. The fact that they were laughing, joking and enduring their vicissitudes with marvelous humor and fortitude would only add to the irony of their absurd suffering. If the journey became too miserable a few might start to ask what it was all about or even attempt to seek a better way of travel. It might even happen that a concerned driver would hit a few extra bumps just to jostle them into thinking.

Just as the body grows strong through exercise, so a viable philosophy of life must come not by settling back and resigning ourselves to the miseries of the journey, but as a vital power released by the effort to think through to the causes of the rigors undertaken. What we are seeking is not some neatly classified timetable of truth, as much as a way to realize the truth in our own experience, and to know why it matters so much that we should find it. We can usually tell if we just "think we're thinking" because it is so easy and we grow overstuffed and complacent in the process. If we are not merely accumulating thoughts, but are directing them creatively toward the transformation of our lives, then the thinking will not be so easy, and we shall have to do something about it. It is not the content of the thought that empowers us, any more than strength can be said to reside in sheer bulk of muscle and bone. Rather it is the coordination and integration of all our resources that will see us through. The world is already turgid with undigested if not indigestible ideas, but there will always be a need for more responsive and responsible human beings.

APPENDIX

Advanced Yoga Positions

1. SALUTE TO THE SUN (Your Daily Dozen)

This ancient salutation to the sun is called "Surya Namas-kar" in Sanskrit, the language of yoga. Traditionally the routine was repeated twelve times in succession, once for each month of the year, each time addressing the sun by a different title of respect. The best time to practice it is in the morning — to greet the sun — but it can be used to invigorate the body at any time, since the sun's power is also considered to radiate from the heart which warms and enlivens the whole system. Insomniacs find it helpful since after completing twelve or more rounds the victim of sleeplessness is usually grateful for bed.

1. Stand erect with your palms together, thumbs against your chest. Pause for a moment and think of the sun as the eternal source of light and power.

2. Inhale as you raise your arms high over your head, bending backward as far as possible.

3. Exhale and bend forward, keeping your knees straight, and touch the floor with fingers on the outside of your feet. Your fingers should not move from this position until you raise them in position 11. Try to touch your forehead to your knees.

4. Inhale, bending left knee while sliding your right foot backward until your almost straight right knee is one inch from the floor. Raise your head, look up as high as possible, and arch your back. Keep your hands and left foot motionless during this position.

5. Retain breath and slide your left foot backward alongside the right foot and straighten your legs, so that your body forms a straight line while you are resting on your toes and palms.

6. Exhale and rest on floor with only your toes, knees, chest, palms and forehead touching. This pose traditionally was called "sastanga namaskar" or eight curved prostration, and it leaves your body poised to move into the next position.

7. Inhale, look up throughout position and keep your neck bent back as you raise your head, then upper chest and finally your lower chest. The lower part of your body remains on the floor from navel down. Your elbows are slightly bent. This should look like the Cobra position.

8. Exhale and raise your hips until your arms and legs are straight. Keep pressing your heels as flat as you can against the floor. Your body should form a ninety degree angle.

9. Inhale and bring your right foot forward between your hands until it is in line with your fingertips. Raise your head, look up and arch your back as in position 4.

10. Exhale and bring your left foot forward between your arms, straighten your legs, and try to touch your head to your knees as in position 3.

11. Inhale, raising your arms over head and stretching backward as in position 2.

12. Exhale, lower arms to your sides and relax.

This is an excellent warm-up routine and is good for general coordination. The separate positions should flow together in a rhythmic pattern of fluid motion. The alternation of forward and backward bending releases tensions and keeps the spine and joints supple.

2. THE HEADSTAND (KING OF EXERCISES)

The Headstand is called king of exercises because just as the king is head of his country, so is the head king of the body. In these days of world confusion we would like to believe that we are at least rulers over ourselves. Yet our self-dominion depends upon the extent to which we are able, not merely to rule over but to communicate with and discipline the body. It is not enough to order it around. We must also create order within. People exaggerate the difficulties of doing the Headstand simply because they are not acquainted with the technique. They fling their feet wildly into the air, take a tumble, and decide that this is not for them. Actually, any healthy person in fairly good condition should be able to master it with a little regular practice. Many people in their sixties and seventies continue to perform it daily. If it proves unduly difficult for you to learn, this should serve as an urgent warning that you are on the downgrade physically and should take immediate action to reverse this decline.

If you have the courage to face up to yourself, this can be your moment of truth. But please read the following instructions thoroughly before attempting to upend yourself and conquer gravity.

First kneel down on a soft carpet or firm mat. Place your palms together lightly, spread fingers, interweave them and clasp your hands. Rest interlocked hands on the floor with little fingers down. Place the back of your head in cupped hands against your fingers so that the top of your head rests on the floor.

Your elbows should be about ten inches apart so that the weight of your body will be distributed along locked fingers, arms and head. If too much pressure is felt on your neck, it is probably because you have allowed your elbows to fly out at the sides, instead of digging them in for support. To position your elbows walk forward on your knees until they are between the elbows. Press elbows against outside of knees. This shows the proper width for elbows and is not part of the Headstand but merely an aid in assuming the correct stance.

Now raise your hips until knees are straight and together and you are balancing on toes, forearms and head. Walk slowly forward on your toes using four-inch steps, keeping knees straight and trying to hold your back as upright as possible. As your knees approach your chest you can bend them slightly, thus allowing you to keep walking until knees are almost touching your chest.

Be sure not to allow your head to buckle under. If you tend to somersault this indicates that your back and neck are not straight and further conditioning such as push-ups or the Cat may be required. Round-shouldered and muscle-bound people have the most difficult time, since it takes longer to develop flexibility than muscle.

If you are a beginner we suggest that you stop at this point, sit on your heels with forehead touching the floor, and relax. If you have negative feelings about your ability to win through this is the time to dispose of them by resolving to persist.

Practice this first stage until you feel confident of your capacity to support the main weight of the body on your forearms, head and elbows. If dizziness or nausea should occur, this is a sign not to rush ahead. These symptoms usually vanish with continued practice. This preliminary "walk-in" is an excellent exercise in itself and confers many of the benefits of the Headstand. Caution must always be used and the novice should not force progress until proficiency has been gained in every step.

For most people the most difficult part of the Headstand is lifting the feet off the floor in a controlled manner. The secret of doing this is to walk forward on your toes keeping the knees as *straight* as possible and concentrate on pointing your buttocks toward the ceiling. Then raise one foot at a time, bending knee until it is almost against your chest and balance is maintained.

If you are progressing correctly your feet will practically lift themselves off the floor. Do not permit your legs to kick up or out and avoid quick or jerky movements. If you fall, it shows you are not performing the preliminary steps correctly, as each stage has its own built-in safety mechanism. Concentrate on what you are doing and remain in control at all times. If some watchful person is willing to stand behind you this may give you confidence, but we do not ordinarily advocate using a wall or support.

Lifting your feet off the ground can be accomplished if you are willing to proceed slowly and not try to raise your legs all the way up, before your neck and arms are prepared. With knees bent and together, slowly point them toward the ceiling keeping your legs doubled up and your back straight.

Only after your knees are pointed directly at the ceiling and you are securely balanced should you straighten your legs and point toes upward. Your legs should be together and the body in a straight line from the tip of your toes to the top of your head.

To come down from the Headstand, reverse the procedure used to get into it. Legs are slowly bent while your knees remain pointed toward the ceiling. Then knees descend toward your chest, but your back stays firmly erect. Lower your toes to the floor by straightening legs. Finish by sitting on your heels as though praying toward Mecca. Hold this position for a few moments to allow your blood circulation to return to normal. Throughout this exercise you should breathe through your nose.

Now that you have read the instructions for doing the Headstand there is one more step we suggest you take before making the attempt.

Kneel down as you would in the preliminary position and mentally visualize yourself going through the motions. Resolve to exert your most concentrated effort. Then go a-head.

If you have a back that is crooked and you practice the Head-stand, nature will try to correct it by forcing you to compensate for any leaning tendency which throws you off balance. Usually after a few months of practice the inclination to offset any curvature has become habitual and the spine has started to straighten of its own accord.

When you first attempt the Headstand you may feel uncomfortable and unable to hold it longer than a few seconds. This is because your kinesthetic sense has not adapted to the upside-down position. Pressing down on the floor with your elbows will facilitate balance. With repeated practice your body will become adjusted to this reversal of its relationship to the earth and thus be better able to endure stresses of all kinds. You will feel yourself becoming a better balanced personality, coping more efficiently with the tensions that upset the equilibrium of body and mind.

Many people derive satisfaction from building up endurance to the point of being able to maintain the Headstand for as long as ten minutes at a time. Three minutes, however, shows considerable proficiency and allows a complete revitalization of the system. The position strengthens the approximately six hundred muscles supporting the body and insures their mutual cooperation in maintaining your back, neck and head in proper alignment. As the stomach is pulled in, abdominal organs, rather than being merely squeezed, are firmly maintained in proper placement.

It is not enough to build up bulging biceps, triceps and pectorals with weight-lifting and calisthenics. One can ripple and flex muscles and still hunch forward in a gorilla-like stance with chin jutting out from a virtually immobilized bull neck. All parts of the body must be knitted together proportionately in the correct posture. The Headstand insures that the shoulders will stay back, the spine straight and legs and hips flexible, so that the whole body is integrated into one harmoniously functioning totality.

VARIATIONS

When the Headstand is performed with the following variations it makes a complete routine which bends your spine forward and backward and maintains resiliency in every part. First practice moving your legs forward and back in a scissor-kick, gradually extending the length of the stretch. Then spread your legs apart to the sides and bring them together in the center. When you can move your legs with ease either way, combine the motions by spreading them wide apart and rotating them from the hips in a circle, wrapping them about each other, and then unwinding and rotating the opposite way.

Try lowering one leg until toes touch the floor. Raise it back and lower the other leg.

Both legs can be lowered with straight knees, until your toes touch the floor, then raised back up again.

Then extend them backward with bent knees so that your spine stretches both ways.

Spread your legs and press soles of feet together.

Lower one foot with sole against inside of other leg until sole rests on side of knee. Raise and lower the other foot the same way.

Then lower leg with sole against shin bone of other leg, until sole rests on kneecap. Repeat on other side.

If really proficient you can cross your legs in the Lotus posture of the yogis while in the Headstand, and raise and lower them in this position.

Finally, you can press your palms to the floor so that you rest only on palms and forearms. Then raise your head upward while bending knees and arching your spine. This position is known as the Scorpion.

These variations make the Headstand a continuing challenge. They are so complete that you could stay physically fit with no other exercise routine. This makes it ideal for sedentary workers who have no time for regular sports or workouts at a gym. Then when vacation comes around you are already in tip-top shape and run no danger of overstraining through unaccustomed exertion.

The Headstand is also useful for the athlete who may be developing a single part of his physique and neglecting the rest. Often golf, bowling, tennis and other recreations which use mainly one arm, build up only one side of the body and cause the muscles to pull unevenly. The Headstand requires no special equipment, financial expenditure or travel — only the will to begin.

TRIPOD HEADSTAND

Older people, children, and those with round shoulders or inflexible necks and hips, often are not ready to practice the Headstand described above, but succeed with the version known as the Tripod. To accomplish this, kneel and place palms down, fingers forward on the floor at shoulder width. Your head should always be placed in front of your fingertips, so that if lines were drawn connecting your head and palms they would form an equilateral triangle. Your forearms should be perpendicular to the floor.

Put your right knee on your right elbow and left knee on your left elbow. From this position knees should be lifted until they point at the ceiling. Straighten your legs, and there you are, upside down. Some people prefer to raise one leg all the way up at once and follow it with the other, skipping the intermediary stage of resting knees on elbows.

The Tripod Headstand puts considerably more strain on your neck than does the forearm version and hence is not appropriate for long-continued holding. It provides an excellent opportunity to acquire the feeling of coordinating your body as a whole and gives the strength to proceed on to the basic forearm Headstand.

Although the Headstand benefits all who practice it, it can prove providential for executives, chairbound chairmen, and all whose mental labors leave little time for activity. Because the position is almost motionless, the muscles of your body are not deprived of life-giving oxygen as would occur after strenuous exertion. The Headstand is safe for normal hearts since it relieves the load and requires minimal expenditure of energy for maximum improvement. It also promotes the elasticity of the approximately sixty thousand miles of arteries and veins in your circulatory system. The network of blood vessels is enriched by the development of auxiliary supply lines so that an increased flow of blood nourishes your heart, brain, glands and vital organs. This collateral circulation is like constructing extra roads in a town, so that if the main highway can not carry the load, traffic can be shunted to alternate routes.

The main thing to remember about your heart is that it is a *muscle*. Like any other muscle it can increase in size and efficiency and be trained to pump more effectively. It can also atrophy from disuse. For this reason increasing numbers of cardiologists are now urging even their postcoronary patients to move about and exercise in order to strengthen the heart. This suggestion would have horrified most doctors only a decade ago, but inactivity may turn out to be the worst heart crippler of all. This is strongly suggested by recent statistics showing that men who lead active lives are less susceptible to heart troubles than their more sedentary counterparts. Common sense bears this out, even when put unscientifically as in the statement made by a durable headstander of our acquaintance who explained, "As long as you are on your feet you are growing older. Standing on your head you reverse the process and grow younger." The Headstand coordinates all parts of your body organizing complex new nerve connections. As more intricate neural pathways are opened up, the mind also opens to fresh ideas. Truly this is the thinking man's exercise. It is simply a matter of being willing to use your head to get ahead.

3. THE FISH

Lie on your back with legs outstretched. Place your fingers under your buttocks, palms down, and raise your chest off the floor using your elbows for support. Tilt your head backward and arch back until the top of your head rests on the floor. Hold up to thirty seconds.

VARIATIONS

a. In Fish position inhale as you slowly raise your arms and stretch them back over your head until your fingers touch the floor behind. Exhale and bring your arms up and down again at your sides. Repeat three times.

b. While in Fish position inhale and slowly raise your head forward until your chin presses against your chest. Exhale and slowly lower your head until the top touches the floor.

Repeat five or more times. This is excellent for preventing or eliminating double chins.

c. Sit on your heels and lean back as in Hip Lift. Lower your back towards the floor until you rest on forearms, elbows and the top of your head. Inhale and stretch arms back over your head until your fingers rest lightly on the floor behind. To get out of this position we suggest you grasp your ankles with your hands and pull yourself up.

d. Cross your legs in the Lotus position and practice the Fish. Your right hand should clasp your left toe and left hand clasp your right toe with elbows pressing on the floor to enable you to arch your back and raise your chest. The top of your head, buttocks and knees remain flat on the floor.

The Fish is particularly good for respiratory problems such as asthma and also for the neck and thyroid gland.

4. SITTING POSITIONS

a. *Head to Knee*

Sit erect with your right leg outstretched and your left leg bent in so that your heel fits into your crotch with sole against your thigh. Gently press your left knee to the floor. Inhale and raise both arms high over your head. Exhale slowly and bend forward trying to touch your right toes. Repeat on other side.

VARIATION

Sit erect with your right leg outstretched and place your left foot on top of your right thigh with heel touching stomach. Inhale and raise your arms high. Exhale and bend forward trying to catch hold of your right toes. Repeat on the other side. If you can accomplish this, practice reaching your arm around your back and grasping the toes of your bent foot. Hold toes and bend forward catching the toes of your outstretched foot as above. Try to hold this position without motion.

b. *Knee to Forehead*

Sit erect with your right heel tucked into crotch. Grasp your left knee with both hands and pull your leg up with straight knee until your forehead touches knee. Keep your back as erect as possible. Advanced students can practice grasping toes instead of knee.

VARIATION

Sit erect with feet out in front and clasp your hands behind your head. Lift your right leg with straight knee as high as you can while bending your head forward until it touches your knee. Repeat, using your left leg. When you can sit with your fingers touching the floor and, lifting one leg, touch it with your forehead you can consider yourself advanced.

c. *Angle Balance*

Sit erect with your legs extended, your knees straight and together, palms on floor. Lean slightly back and raise both legs with straight knees. Balance on the end of your spine for fifteen seconds.

VARIATIONS

Sit erect with your knees tucked into your chest and feet flat on floor. Pull your legs into your chest as much as you can by clasping your hands around your legs. Keeping legs against your chest inhale as you raise your arms and stretch them high in back of you at shoulder level.

Sitting as above grasp your toes with palms against little toes, arms on outside of legs. Slowly straighten your legs until your knees are straight. Balance this way for thirty seconds. Advanced students can rock back and forward in this position, maintaining balance.

d. *Upper Leg Stretch*

Sit erect and place the soles of your feet together. Use your hands to pull your heels toward you until they are almost touching the crotch. Then place your hands on your knees and press down until your legs are flat on the ground. Finally, clasp your toes with your fingers and lower your forehead until it touches the floor.

For extra stretching of your thighs, spread your legs wide apart, then thrust your arms backward under your knees, palms down, while lowering your head to the floor in front. This ultimate stretch is called the Tortoise.

e. *The Lotus*

In a seated position bend your left leg, placing your foot on your right thigh, pulling your ankle forward until your heel touches your stomach. Then bend your right leg toward your left knee. Grasp your right ankle and slowly lift it up over your left knee until it rests on your left thigh. Your soles should be turned up with both knees touching floor. Keep your back straight. Practice this position until it becomes comfortable and you enjoy sitting this way. This pose can be used when doing Alternate Breathing.

f. *The Bound Lotus*

To vary the Lotus, reach your arms around your back so that your right hand clasps your left toe and your left hand clasps your right toe. Holding your toes, bend forward until your forehead touches the floor.

5. SHOOTING BOW POSITIONS

a. *Cross Bow*

In a sitting position with your legs extended in front, reach forward and grasp your right toe with your left hand. It is important that your thumb be on the sole of your foot, your fingers on top of your toes, with straight wrist and palm against big toe, so that you can lift the foot up rather than pull it. Lift your right toes, bending right knee in order to raise your toes to your left ear. At the same time grasp the toes of your left foot with your right hand, keeping your left knee straight. Keep lifting your right toes toward the left ear for ten seconds. Then reverse sides.

b. *Curved Bow*

You can also practice the Bow by using your left hand to lift left toes to left ear, while your right hand clasps toes of your straight right foot. Repeat on other side.

c. *Bow and Arrow*

Advanced archers can pull one leg back as in the Curved Bow, and then straighten the bent leg and raise it as high as possible.

The Shooting Bow positions keep all the lower joints flexible, build up arms and shoulders and stretch your thigh muscles.

6. INCLINED PLANE

From a sitting position place your palms on the floor a foot behind you with your fingers pointed back. Knees and elbows should remain straight throughout this exercise. Raise your hips until your body forms a straight line. Your feet should remain flat on the floor so that the weight of your body rests entirely on your soles and palms. Hold this position fifteen seconds or more, allowing no sagging in the midsection.

VARIATION

When you can maintain the Inclined Plane without sagging, allow your head to tilt backward and raise your right leg with straight knee as high as you can. Repeat, alternating legs. This position is sometimes called the Rack and can also be done facing the floor, or with your side to the floor. It is best practiced immediately after Forward Bending exercises in order to reverse the stretching action and remove kinks from your back.

7. BACK BENDING EXERCISES

a. *The Swan*

This is similar to the Cobra except that you raise your head higher and bend your knees, pressing your head back toward your heels. Arms are straight so that your weight is suspended from palms and knees. Hold up to one-half minute. Afterward sit back on your heels and bend forward until your forehead touches the floor in front of your knees. Without moving either palms or knees practice moving from the Swan to the Heel Sitting position and back again, slowly, so that your spine stretches first one way and then the other.

b. *Pelvic Stretch*

This position has many variations and you can select the most suitable ones. First, kneel and stretch your arms behind your head in order to warm up. Then, in kneeling position, clasp your ankles so that your thumbs face one another. When you can hold this position for thirty seconds or more, tilt

your head back and slowly lower head, bending elbows simultaneously, until your head touches the floor and your forearms are flat on the floor. Keep your back arched. Try to return to the starting position without letting go of your ankles, by pushing down on the floor with your elbows, keeping your back arched, and pulling forward with your leg muscles.

VARIATIONS

A variation of this stretch is to place your palms on the top or side of your thighs and lower your head backward, without using your arms, until it touches the floor.

You can also stretch your spine by kneeling and lying back with your arms extended back over your head. For an extra stretch place your palms on the floor, one on each side of your head at shoulder width, and raise your hips and body as high as possible. Push your head as close to your heels as you can. This is called the Diamond and it is a rough one.

c. *The Wheel*

Lie on your back and bend knees until heels touch your buttocks with soles flat on the floor. Place one hand on each side of your head, palms down and fingers pointing toward your shoulders. Raise your body and head by pushing down with your hands and feet, keeping feet flat on floor. When you can hold this posture without straining, endeavor to raise one leg or arm at a time, as high as possible. With practice you will be able to move your hands closer to your heels so that your body resembles a wheel. Extremely supple people can do the Wheel by bending backward from a standing position.

d. *The Limbo*

Kneel and extend your right foot out in front of you with sole on the floor and knee straight. Lunge forward, bending right knee, until your front lower leg is perpendicular to floor, while raising your arms high over head and arching your spine backward. Repeat on the other side. You can vary this position by turning your trunk from the waist and looking toward the leg in back of you with arms forming a circle high over your head.

8. THE TWIST

Sit with your right leg outstretched and bend your left leg in until the heel fits into the crotch. Then raise and bend your right leg and cross it over the left, so that your right sole rests flat on the floor, on the left side of your left knee. Now swing your left arm across the front of your body so that your straight left elbow touches the right side of your right knee and your left fingers grasp your right ankle.

Turn your head and eyes to the right as much as possible and keep looking over your right shoulder. Finally, reach your right arm around your back at waist level and try to touch the inner side of your right thigh. You should endeavor to stay balanced upright and not tip to one side. Arms, head and upper torso all turn to the right while your folded legs keep your lower parts firmly anchored. Repeat, using other side.

This is not the footloose and fanny-free "twist" of modern days, but a carefully controlled contortion stretching your spine from stem to stern.

9. ARM EXERCISES

a. *The Crow*

Squatting on your toes, extend your arms straight down between your legs and put your fingers forward with palms flat on the floor about a shoulder's width apart. Your knees should be outside your elbows and project about three inches in front of them. Keep your lower arms straight, *head down,* and bend your elbows. Rise up on your toes and balance with your knees on *top* of your elbows. Try to hold them there without sliding down the outer sides of your arms. Be sure not to allow your arms to buckle out or back. If your forearms remain straight a great deal of strength is not required. This position demands coordination and control more than brute force, and can, therefore, be done as easily by women as by men. We call the Crow done with the legs in the Lotus position the Crocus.

b. *The Crowbar*

Once you have mastered the Crow you will not find it unduly difficult to balance with both legs on the same side. Squat, and position both knees together over the elbow you intend to use for support. Let your upper legs rest on top of your bent elbow and try to maintain balance. As you become more proficient you can straighten your legs in this position.

The Crow and Crowbar strengthen and coordinate wrists, arms and shoulders and develop the chest. They help prepare for the Headstand, especially when your neck needs to be strengthened without direct pressure.

c. *The Peacock*

Kneel down with your arms between your legs, palms flat on the floor butting against each other, with your fingers pointing backward (opposite from the Crow). Bend your elbows and walk forward on your knees until elbows are as far as possible below your navel, so that your shoulders hunch over your arms. Rest forehead on the floor and straighten your legs until you are supported by your head, arms and toes. Then raise your head and feet simultaneously until your body is parallel to the floor and you are balancing on your arms. Hold this position ten to twenty seconds.

VARIATIONS

The Peacock may be performed by bringing your head down in front and raising your legs behind — like a peacock's tail. A few people with powerful hands can balance on fists or even fingers. The Peacock practiced with your legs in the Lotus position makes balancing much easier.

The Peacock strengthens your back and abdominal muscles, improves digestion and elimination, and tones up all the vital organs. It stimulates the flow of blood to your head and throughout your body. This exercise is advanced but worth trying if you can master the Crow.

d. *The Cock*

In Lotus position place your palms on the floor. Straighten your elbows, raise your buttocks off the floor and try to swing back and forth. Then lower yourself and insert your arms between your calf muscles and thigh (in front of feet) as far as the elbows. Now raise your body as high as possible off the ground while balancing on your palms.

The Cock exercises wrists, hands and arms, but requires proficiency in the Lotus.

10. TOE BALANCING

a. *Hunkering*

Squat down and balance on your toes with your legs together and hands resting on hips. Practice until you can maintain this position with ease. You will feel how all the muscles in your feet work together to keep you balanced. When you are sure of your ability to maintain equilibrium, sit back flat on your feet with your heels firmly pressed against the floor. Return to your original position and repeat several times.

If sitting back on the heels is difficult for you the position can be made easier by extending your arms out in front and spreading your feet farther apart.

b. *Half Hunkering*

Balance on your toes. Then lift your left foot and rest it on your right thigh. If necessary use your hands for support. Now try to balance without using your hands. Some people find it easier to balance if they focus on one particular spot or object. Finally, raise your hands over your head and press your palms together, fingers pointing upward. Repeat, balancing on your left foot.

This position is extremely helpful for people with flat feet, swollen ankles and varicose veins.

11. STANDING POSITIONS

a. *The Stork*

Stand on your right foot with your knee straight and bend your left leg until your left foot rests against the groin of your right leg. Inhale and reach your arms high over your head, pressing palms together and hold. Repeat on the other side. This is the first stage of the Stork. Also try to do the Stork with your eyes shut.

If you can balance in the upward stretching position try to bring both hands down to the ground and press your head against your straight right knee, the whole time keeping your bent left leg tucked up snugly in your groin. Follow through by straightening your body and reaching up again before releasing your bent leg.

Supple people can perform the Stork by reaching the left arm around the back to catch hold of the toes of bent left leg, and continuing to clasp toes throughout all stages.

b. *The Eagle*

From a standing position swing your right leg around the front of the supporting left leg, wrapping your right ankle around lower left leg until your right toes point front just above the inner side of left ankle. While in this position intertwine your arms and balance with your hands at chin level. Repeat, balancing on the right leg.

When you can maintain this first balance easily, bend forward until your chin rests upon your bent upper leg so that your entire body is folded inward and you take on the attitude of an eagle. Hold five seconds and then slowly straighten up.

c. *The Vulture*

This position is called the Vulture because it involves swooping down to the floor — albeit in slow motion. Take your perch with legs widespread, clasp your hands behind your back, and bend your right knee in a deep lunge. As you lunge down bring your forehead as close as possible to your right toes and hold. Your shoulders will be in front of your right knee. Come back up slowly and repeat, lunging to the left.

This is an excellent exercise for skiers. It gives strength and pliability to your ankles and legs and improves balance.

12. SPECIAL PURPOSE EXERCISES

a. *The Lion*

Kneel and sit back on your heels with your arms stiffly outstretched, hands resting on knees with fingers widespread. Inhale deeply. Then exhale through your mouth with full force, tensing your whole body while rolling your eyes upward and curling your tongue out and downward as far as possible. Hold for about fifteen seconds.

This is a peculiar sort of lion, but when you feel a virus coming on you will be grateful for the magical potency of the Lion to keep you from lyin' in bed. The Lion brings a rush of blood to your throat, head and upper chest region enabling you to throw off incipient sore throats and colds.

b. *The Elephant*

Stand erect with your left hand on your waist. Inhale and bend forward allowing your right arm to dangle in front of you until your right shoulder feels completely relaxed. Allow your fingers to swing back and forth just above the floor, like an elephant's trunk. Then inhale deeply and swing your trunk (right arm) in a wide arc, up and back, stretching it behind you. Hold for several seconds with your whole body stretching back. Exhale, relax, and repeat on other side.

VARIATION

The Elephant can be varied by swinging both arms together down and then back up over your head, stretching backward, first on one side and then on the other.

We have found this exercise to be an effective all-purpose conditioner, and remarkably helpful for alleviating bursitis.

c. *The Mountain*

In a standing or sitting position raise your arms high over your head, press your palms flat together and hold for a minute or until your arms start to ache. Keep pressing palms up and elbows back.

As easy as this position sounds it is remarkably effective in improving posture and relieving tension in the neck and shoulders. Make it a handy health habit.

d. *The Flower*

Clench your hands with thumb outside fingers. Feel the hardness of your fists, like the tight buds of early spring. Visualize the life-force pulsing through your arms and forcing its way up into your wrists and palms. Slowly, as though growing from within, your fingers will begin to loosen and your hands open. Take a full minute to allow your fingers to spread wide, curving outward in petallike form, until they are stretching to their utmost limit.

Then allow another minute to let the flower fade back into the tight hard seedpod form as your fingers close in again. Clench your fingers briefly, then shake them out and relax. If you have performed this exercise properly your face will be glowing from the effort and you may even perspire.

The Flower is another handy health habit for arthritic fingers. Just as an object cools from the outside so, with aging, the joints in the extremities tend to harden and lose their circulation. Therefore it is important to keep them active and alive.

e. *Eye Exercises*

With your face pointed forward, look as far as possible to the right, moving only your eyes. Locate a spot and focus on it. Then look to the left. Alternate three to five times and rest. Take a deep breath and imagine that you are breathing in through your eyes.

Repeat as above, looking far up and down. Again imagine yourself taking a deep breath through your eyes.

Repeat, moving your eyes diagonally, first upper right to lower left and back, then lower right to upper left and back. Again breathe in through your eyes.

Repeat, tracing upper and lower semicircles, and then full circles, three times each way.

Eye exercises may be varied by imagining a huge clock and fixing your gaze on successive numbers. Focus on each imaginary number in clockwise order, rest and return counterclockwise back to number twelve.

Be sure to end by palming your eyes. Rest the palms of your hands over your eyes, fingers pointing up, for thirty seconds while you breathe deeply and visualize golden energy streaming through the region of your eyes.

Forward Bend at The End

Try to end with a simple stretch and bending routine, always inhaling as you reach up and exhaling as you bend down. You can vary this exercise by spreading your legs, clasping your arms behind you, and bending from the waist, bringing your forehead down first to one knee, then up and down to the other knee. You can also lower your upraised arms touching the floor first on one side of your feet, up, then down on the other side. Finish with a long upward stretch and then practice the deep relaxation of Floating (pg. 88) outlined in the chapter called *Your Basic Routine*.

EXERCISE INDEX